Little Magic Horse

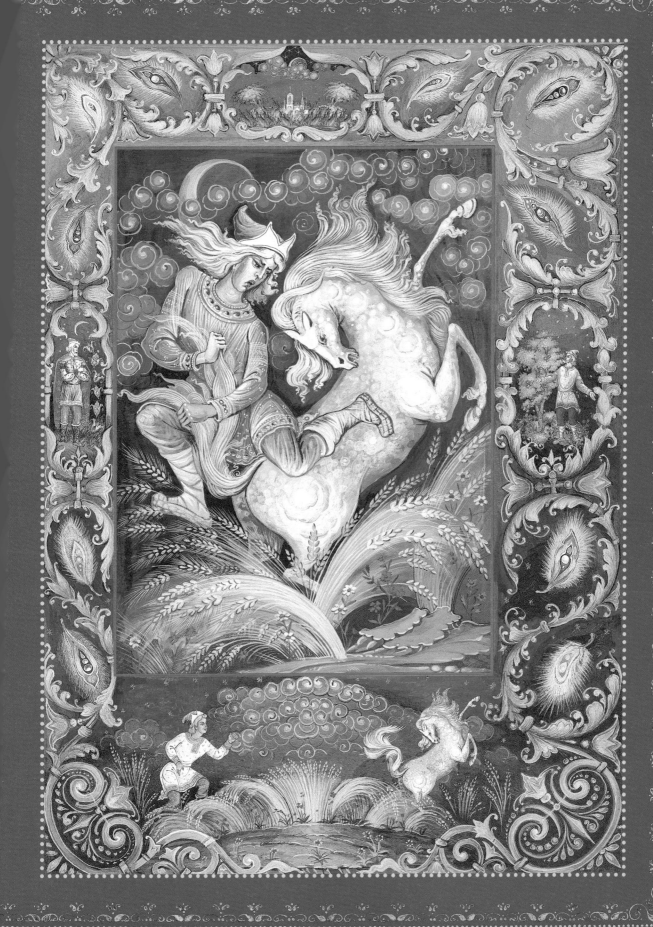

Pyotr Yershov

Little Magic Horse

Illustrations by
Vladimir Nemov

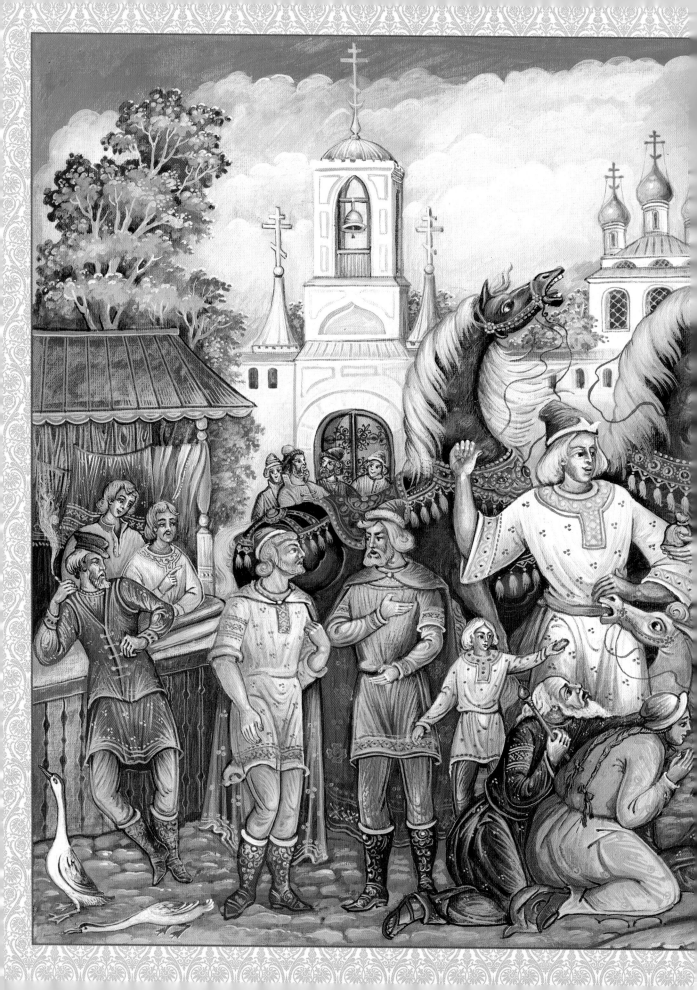

Part I

Now then, our tale begins.

Over many hills and dales,
Far beyond the seas and vales,
Opposite the sky, on earth
Lived an old man from his birth,
With three sons. The eldest one
Was the village paragon.
Number two ran as to rule,
While the youngest was a fool.
All the brothers farmed, sowed grain,
Traveled to a near domain
Whose renowned metropolis
Made a pleasant trip of this.
There they traded, sold their wheat—
And, with moneybags replete,
Home returned well pleased with what
They thought not too bad a lot.

In the course of time's advance
There befell them a mischance.
Some marauder came to pillage,
Shake the young wheat in their tillage.
And the poor folk since their birth
Had not met such wrong on earth.
So they thought and planned till they
Had determined on a way
To surprise him at his pillage—
Catch this thief. They'd guard their tillage
Nightly; they'd patrol their bread,
Seal the vandal's doom instead.

With the setting of the sun
Went the brave and eldest one
To stand guard and ne'er relax
With his pitchfork and his ax.
Dark and stormy fell the night,
And he, overcome with fright,
Hid where it was safe and soft,
Spent his vigil in a loft.
When, however, morning broke,
Then the watcher stanch awoke.

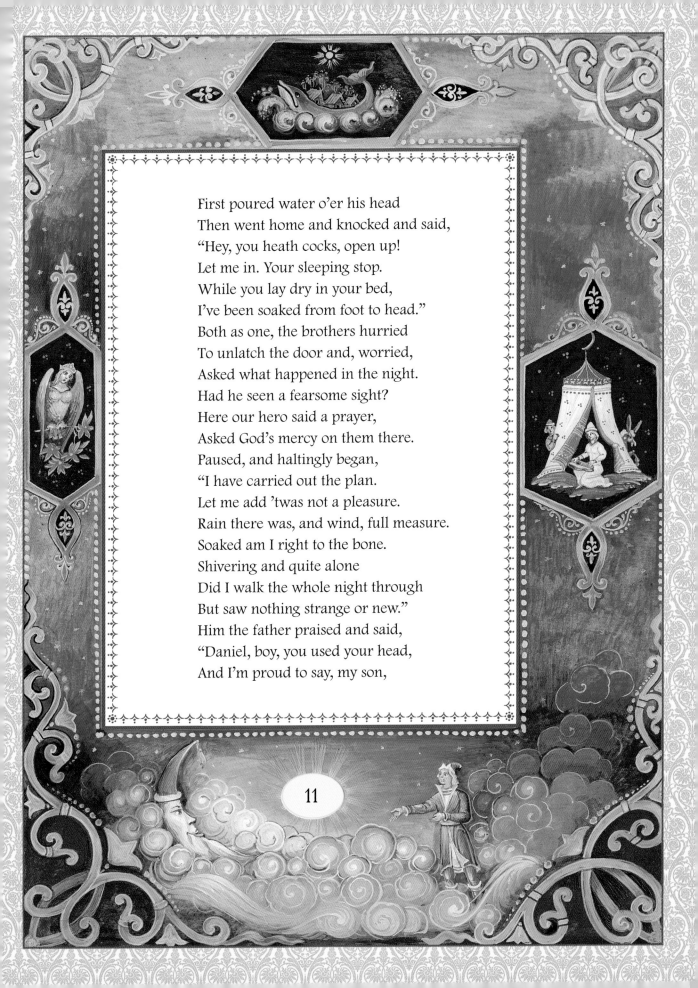

First poured water o'er his head
Then went home and knocked and said,
"Hey, you heath cocks, open up!
Let me in. Your sleeping stop.
While you lay dry in your bed,
I've been soaked from foot to head."
Both as one, the brothers hurried
To unlatch the door and, worried,
Asked what happened in the night.
Had he seen a fearsome sight?
Here our hero said a prayer,
Asked God's mercy on them there.
Paused, and haltingly began,
"I have carried out the plan.
Let me add 'twas not a pleasure.
Rain there was, and wind, full measure.
Soaked am I right to the bone.
Shivering and quite alone
Did I walk the whole night through
But saw nothing strange or new."
Him the father praised and said,
"Daniel, boy, you used your head,
And I'm proud to say, my son,

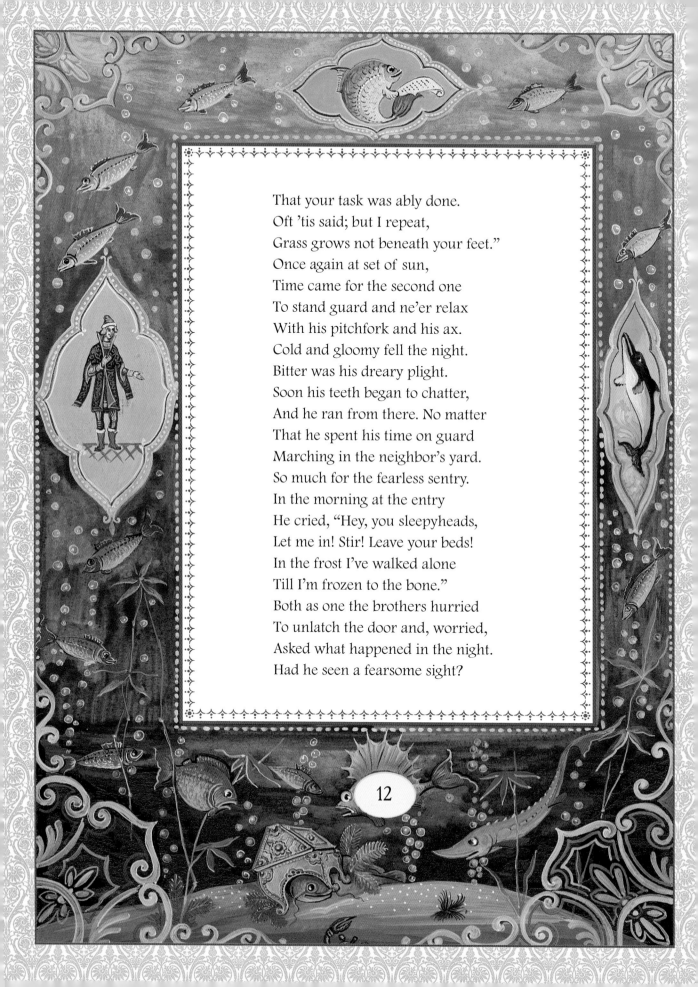

That your task was ably done.
Oft 'tis said; but I repeat,
Grass grows not beneath your feet."
Once again at set of sun,
Time came for the second one
To stand guard and ne'er relax
With his pitchfork and his ax.
Cold and gloomy fell the night.
Bitter was his dreary plight.
Soon his teeth began to chatter,
And he ran from there. No matter
That he spent his time on guard
Marching in the neighbor's yard.
So much for the fearless sentry.
In the morning at the entry
He cried, "Hey, you sleepyheads,
Let me in! Stir! Leave your beds!
In the frost I've walked alone
Till I'm frozen to the bone."
Both as one the brothers hurried
To unlatch the door and, worried,
Asked what happened in the night.
Had he seen a fearsome sight?

Here our hero said a prayer,
Asked God's mercy on them there.
And, still shivering, began,
"I have carried out the plan.
Luckless was my ill-starred fate.
Fierce the cold did penetrate
To the marrow of each bone.
Through the night I froze alone
But did find naught else to do
And saw nothing strange or new."
And to him the father said,
"Gabriel, son, you used your head."

For the third time sets the sun.
Time comes for the youngest one
To stand guard, but he'll not move,
He sits singing on the stove,
Bellows lustily and sighs
Over "Beautiful Soft Eyes."
So the brothers urge and nudge him.
Nothing they can say will budge him.
For he doesn't wish to yield,
Take his turn to watch the field.

So at last the father broaches
The sore subject, and approaches
Him, beseeching, "Listen, Johnny,
Take your turn and stand guard, sonny.
Then I'll buy you new blue jeans,
Give you extra peas and beans."
Johnny rises, limp and slack,
Throws his sheepskin on his back,
Stuffs a bread crust next his chest,
Starts his vigil like the rest.
John patrolled the field. The night
Softly fell. The moon shone bright.
Looking round him, in the hush,
John sat down behind a bush,
Idly counted stars, and just
Nibbled calmly at his crust.
Midnight, and a horse's neigh,
Made him rise. Without delay,
Curious, searching here and there,
He at length espied a mare.
And the mare he saw was so
White as winter's freshest snow.
And a marvel to behold

15

Fell her mane of tight-curled gold.
"Oh-ho-ho! So this is who
Is this thief! Just wait. Can you
Guess I never fool or play?
Mounting you is more my way.
What a locust! I'll calm down!"
And a moment scarce had flown
When he overtook the mare,
Grabbed her tail's soft curling hair,
And had mounted. But, alack,
He had mounted front to back.
She, swift startled from her grazing,
With her deep eyes fiercely blazing
Arched her neck and fled as though
Sped the arrow from a bow,
Circled widely o'er each plain,
Bucked across each dale in vain,
Galloped headlong on each hill,
Rearing, walked the woods until
Hook or crook should somehow guide her
To unseat the stubborn rider.
But our John sat firm and bland,
Tight her tail grasped in his hand.

16

Wearied, she at last stood calm.
And so spoke to him, "Now, John,
It is mete that you should own
Me. Find me a place to rest
And look after me as best
You are able. And take care,
As three dawns rise bright and fair,
Let me out to roam at will
O'er the meadow and the hill.
When three days have passed, I'll bear
You two steeds so wondrous rare
That of them no single word
Has been spoken, dreaded, or heard.
And, besides, I'll bear a pony
Ten hands high and rather homely.
Yard-long ears he'll have, and bumps
On his back like camel humps.
You may sell the pair, of course,
But don't trade the little horse
For a fancy belt or cap,
Lose him in a game of crap.
Not on earth not underground
Will such loyalty be found.

18

Warmth he'll bring in wintry clime,
Stir a breeze in summertime;
Should you hunger, fetch your bread;
Should you thirst, some mead instead.
As for me, I'll roam the plain
Free to try my strength again."
So, thinks John. "Quite fine, if true."
Meanwhile quickly drives her to
An old cattle shed; what's more,
Hangs some burlap o'er the door.
And as soon as day does come
Wends his cheerful way toward home,
Singing loud a rousing song
Of a "Gallant Brave and Strong."

Mounts the steps up to the stoop,
Takes the knocker by the loop,
Knocks with such an awful din
That the roof almost caves in.
Shouts as though afire had spread
Loud enough to wake the dead.
Both the brothers in dismay
Leap from bed and, stuttering, say,

19

"Who dares knack so loud? Have done."
"I, your brother, foolish John."

They make haste to let him in,
Swing the door wide and begin
To upbraid him for the scare,
Asking him, how did he dare?
John, however, does not lose
Time in doffing coat or shoes;
To his favored stove retires,
Quite prepared to talk; desires
To weave tales about his plight
And the happenings in the night.

"All night long, unsleeping, I
Counted stars up in the sky,
And the moon I think, that night,
Shone with its uncertain light.
Suddenly, Old Nick appeared!
He had whiskers and a beard,
Looked just like an alley cat;
Eyes like saucers, round and flat.
Fast he galloped, while his feet

And his tail beat down the wheat.
I'm not one to fool or play;
Mounting him was more my way.
Long he galloped; far he fled,
Almost broke my neck and head.
Still I managed, kept my seat,
Clung to him with hands and feet.
Till at last the sly one tired,
Begged my mercy, and conspired,
'If you let me live on earth,
Promise I a whole year's worth
Of behaviour so designed
As to benefit mankind.'
Hoping I had rightly heard,
I took Satan at his word."
At this point the teller stopped.
Yawned just once, in slumber dropped.
Long the brothers kept straight faces;
They laughed fit to burst their braces
Now, and held their sides as well
At the tale they'd heard him tell.
Laughed the father, 'spite his years,
Till his cheeks were wet with tears,

Though to be so uncontrolled
Is unseemly in the old.

Whether little time or much
Passed, since John had stood his watch,
Not a rumor have I heard.
No one's told me, not a word.
But it's not for us to worry
If a year or two should hurry
Past, since time has always flown.
So our story carries on.

So it happened that one day
(I recall the holiday)
Daniel, tipsy, tired, half dead,
Lurched into the cattle shed.
And he sees? Stand wondrous there
Two steeds, golden-maned and rare,
And, besides, a plaything pony
Ten hands high and rather homely;
Yard-long ears he has, and bumps
On his back like camel humps.
"Now I see why foolish John

Spent his nights in here alone."
To himself so Daniel said,
For the shock had cleared his head.
Sobered, he ran home to tell
What he saw to Gabriel.
"Come and see the wondrous pair—
Steeds with manes of golden hair;
That's what foolish John hides out,
Steeds as you've never dreamed about."
Daniel, Gabriel, eager flustered,
With what strength their swift
                         legs mustered
Made a beeline through the bramble,
Barefoot through the thorns did scramble.

After they had stumbled thrice,
Stopped to focus each eye twice,
Gently rubbing here and there,
They at last approached the pair
That stands snorting, neighing too.
Burn their eyes of sapphire blue,
Tightly curled with moonlight pale
Falls each horse's golden tail.

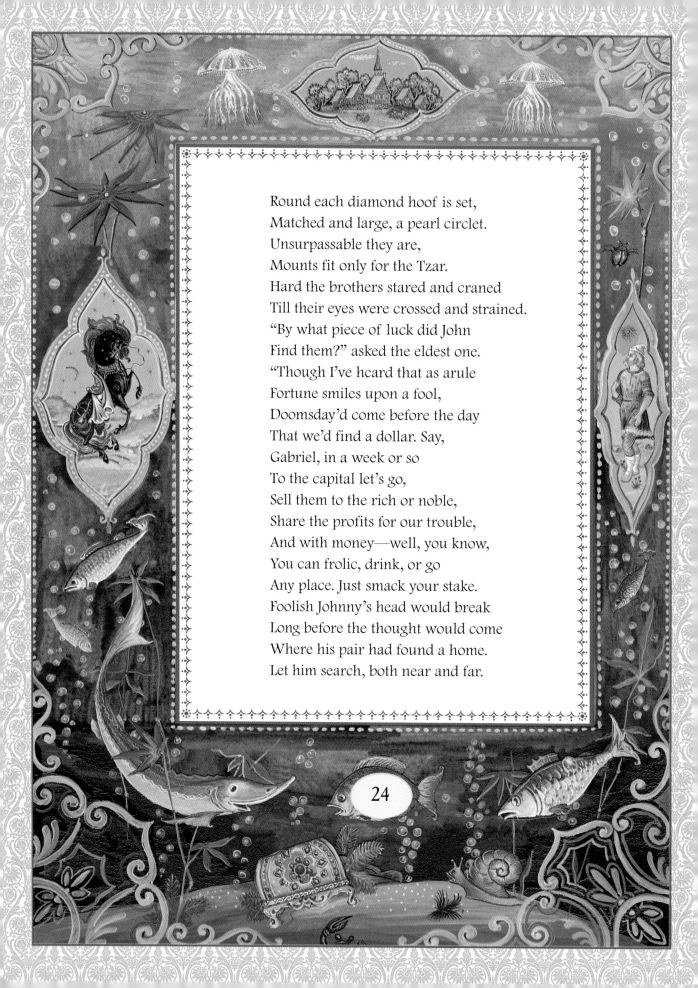

Round each diamond hoof is set,
Matched and large, a pearl circlet.
Unsurpassable they are,
Mounts fit only for the Tzar.
Hard the brothers stared and craned
Till their eyes were crossed and strained.
"By what piece of luck did John
Find them?" asked the eldest one.
"Though I've heard that as arule
Fortune smiles upon a fool,
Doomsday'd come before the day
That we'd find a dollar. Say,
Gabriel, in a week or so
To the capital let's go,
Sell them to the rich or noble,
Share the profits for our trouble,
And with money—well, you know,
You can frolic, drink, or go
Any place. Just smack your stake.
Foolish Johnny's head would break
Long before the thought would come
Where his pair had found a home.
Let him search, both near and far.

24

Shake on it, Conspirator."
So the brothers in accord
Crossed themselves, without a word
Hugged each other, and went home.
On the way they whispered some;
Talked of horses, of a feast;
Guessed about the wonder-beast.

Time flies swiftly on its way,
Hour by hour and day by day;
Soon a week or so has flown,
And the brothers start for town.
There to trade their usual stock
And inquire, too, at the dock
If the Germans'd made a trip
To the hilltown in their ship,
If the heathen Emperor planned
To harass their Christian land.
First they kneel and say a prayer,
Their aged father's blessing share.
Then in stealth each takes a steed
And departs at topmost speed.
Twilight deepens; evening falls;

25

John decides that slumber calls,
Walks the roadway to the shed,
Sings, and gnaws a crust of bread.
When he nears his field of land,
Arms akimbo, feeling grand,
With a swaggering dandy's tread
Sideways walks into the shed.
Though at first all seemed serene,
Gone as though they'd never been
Were the steeds. Before him only
Humpy pranced. The little pony
Clapped his ears in joy and beat
Rhythmic capers with his feet.
Stunned, our Johnny wept and pled,
Leaning 'gainst the cattle shed,
"Tell me, chestnut steeds and gray;
Golden-maned steeds, tell me pray;
Tell me, did I not caress you?
What fiend stole you to possess you?
May he die, the cur, for this,
Perish in some deep abyss!
And of misery have no dearth
Even when he leaves this earth!

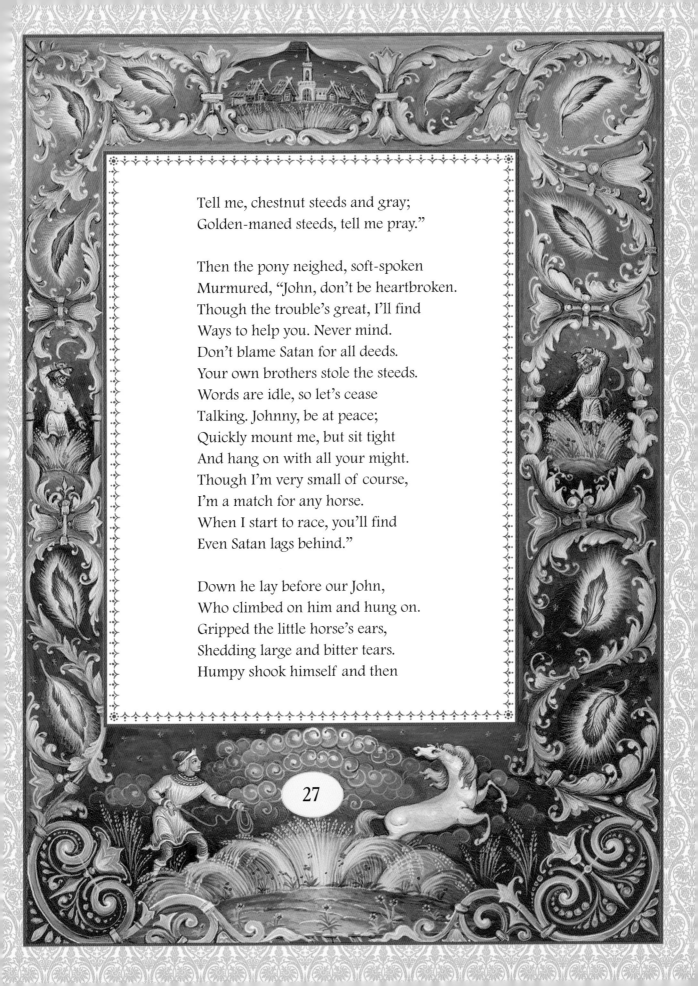

Tell me, chestnut steeds and gray;
Golden-maned steeds, tell me pray."

Then the pony neighed, soft-spoken
Murmured, "John, don't be heartbroken.
Though the trouble's great, I'll find
Ways to help you. Never mind.
Don't blame Satan for all deeds.
Your own brothers stole the steeds.
Words are idle, so let's cease
Talking. Johnny, be at peace;
Quickly mount me, but sit tight
And hang on with all your might.
Though I'm very small of course,
I'm a match for any horse.
When I start to race, you'll find
Even Satan lags behind."

Down he lay before our John,
Who climbed on him and hung on.
Gripped the little horse's ears,
Shedding large and bitter tears.
Humpy shook himself and then

27

Rose and shook himself again.
Snorted, tossed his mane, and fled
Swift as ever arrow sped.
And beneath him and behind
Thick the dust churned in the wind.
In a flash the chase had ended
And the thieves were apprehended.

Both the brothers shook from fright,
Stood bewildered at their plight.
So John shouted his appeal,
"Brothers, shame that you should steal.
Though John's not as wise as you,
He is honest through and through.
Never would he steal a steed."
So the elder spoke, "No need
To deny that we're at fault.
Johnny, you're the very salt
Of the earth. Your pardon give.
Think how poor the life we live.
Even though we work, sow wheat,
Oft we've scarce enough to eat.
If the harvest's lean, confess

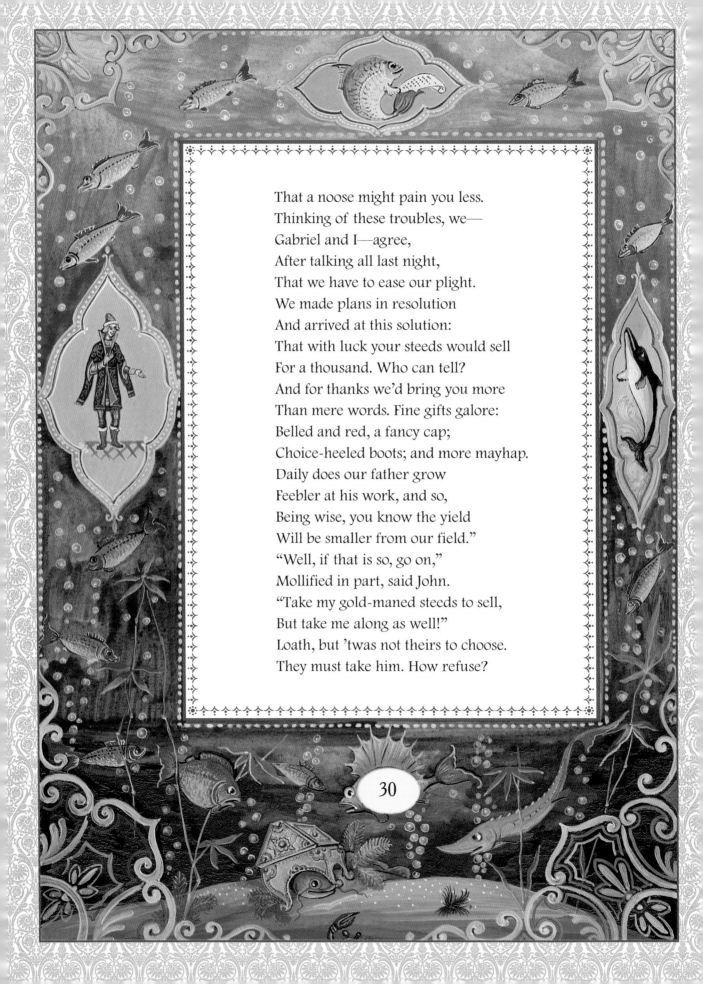

That a noose might pain you less.
Thinking of these troubles, we—
Gabriel and I—agree,
After talking all last night,
That we have to ease our plight.
We made plans in resolution
And arrived at this solution:
That with luck your steeds would sell
For a thousand. Who can tell?
And for thanks we'd bring you more
Than mere words. Fine gifts galore:
Belled and red, a fancy cap;
Choice-heeled boots; and more mayhap.
Daily does our father grow
Feebler at his work, and so,
Being wise, you know the yield
Will be smaller from our field."
"Well, if that is so, go on,"
Mollified in part, said John.
"Take my gold-maned steeds to sell,
But take me along as well!"
Loath, but 'twas not theirs to choose.
They must take him. How refuse?

30

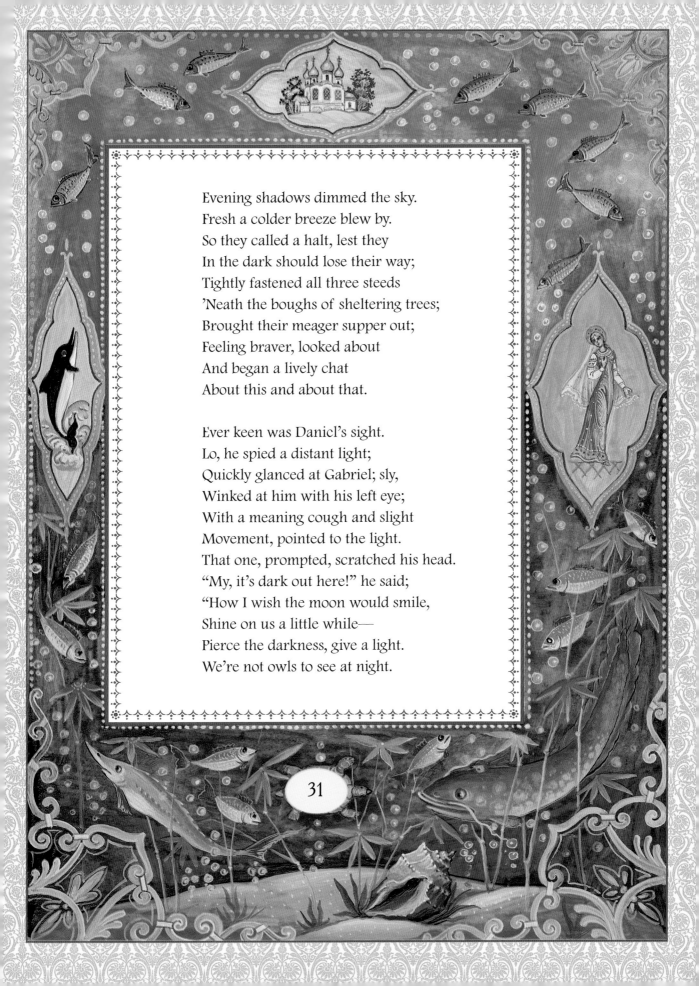

Evening shadows dimmed the sky.
Fresh a colder breeze blew by.
So they called a halt, lest they
In the dark should lose their way;
Tightly fastened all three steeds
'Neath the boughs of sheltering trees;
Brought their meager supper out;
Feeling braver, looked about
And began a lively chat
About this and about that.

Ever keen was Danicl's sight.
Lo, he spied a distant light;
Quickly glanced at Gabriel; sly,
Winked at him with his left eye;
With a meaning cough and slight
Movement, pointed to the light.
That one, prompted, scratched his head.
"My, it's dark out here!" he said;
"How I wish the moon would smile,
Shine on us a little while—
Pierce the darkness, give a light.
We're not owls to see at night.

Wait! I think that I can see
Smoke—or so it seems to be—
Over there.... It's smoke all right.
Say, a fire would make things bright!
What a piece of luck! Oh, John,
Run and fetch a light, just one.
For, to tell the truth, have I
Neither match nor flint to try."
Daniel thinks, ne'er turns a hair,
"How I wish you'd perish there!"
Gabriel speaks aside, "Who knows
Just whose fire distant glows,
That of thieves or honest men?
We'll not hear of him again!"

Nothing's much for foolish John.
He finds Humpy and climbs on,
Pounds his curved sides with his feet,
Pats him with a measured beat.
Humpy rears. John shouts. The pair
Seems to vanish in the air.
"May the Lord protect us here!"
Murmured Gabriel in fear,

32

Crossed himself, shook in each limb.
"Satan must be under him!"

As they neared the fire's source,
Faster ran the little horse.
Soon a field before them lay
Lit as brightly as by day.
But, miraculous to repeat,
There was neither smoke nor heat.
John demanded, wonder-struck,
"Old Nick's doing? Some bad luck?
It burns bright enough, but where
Is the heat and smoke from there?
It's some magic fire, of course!"

"Nonsense," said the little horse.
"It's not magic; it's a feather
From a Firebird. 'Twere far better
For your happiness and lot
If you'd leave it. Take it not,
For you'll find unrest, heartbreak,
Closely follow in its wake."
"Now you've said your say, have done,"

Muttered low the foolish one.
He picked up the Firebird's feather,
Wrapped it in a cloth, together
Hid the treasure in his hat,
Turned the pony back with that.
He arrived, rejoined the others.
To the queries of his brothers
So replied, "I galloped where
Shone the light, found smoldering there
An old stump. With all my might
Did I strain to make a light.
For an hour I blew and tried,
But no use-the old thing died."
Wide-awake the brothers kept,
Laughed at John, and hardly slept.
While John, sheltered 'neath the cart,
Slept all night, snored from the start.

Morning, and they harness up,
Reach the city, and then stop
Opposite the tents, of course,
In the row for trading horse.
It is customary there

For the marshal to declare
If one is to buy or not
Or to sell what one has brought.
Midday scattering the crowd—
Rides the marshal, grand and proud,
Slippered, and fur-hatted. Then
Rides his guard, a hundred men.
Long-nosed solemn, at his side,
Does a bearded herald ride,
Blows his golden trumpet, and
Shouts to the assembled band,
"Traders, open up! Unlock!
You may buy and sell your stock.
Supervisors, take your places
Near the shops—so no disgraces,
Undue noise, or too much crowding
Will result in riots or rowing;
So no swindler's ugly face
Cheats the honest populace."
And each trader fast prepares,
Lures the people, shouts his wares.
"Come, good people, lend an ear!
See what we have over here!

Ours is finest! Ours is best!
Ours outshines that of the rest!"
And the buyers troop to buy
What the traders hawk and cry.
Traders count their hoards like misers,
Winking at the supervisors.

The detachment soon, of course,
Neared the row for trading horse,
Where there was an awful crush.
People milled and tried to push,
Shoved and swarmed as thick as bees,
Laughed and shouted, slapped their knees.
And the marshal was amazed
At the scene on which he gazed
And commanded that his men
Clear a passage for him then.
"Hey, you loafers, don't delay!
Move along! Make way! Make way!"
Cried the guards through whiskered lips
And then smartly cracked their whips.
And the populace complied,
Bared its head, and stepped aside.

And before his eyes a pair
Of breath-taking steeds stands there.
Young, black as the raven's wing,
To each neck gold ringlets cling,
Shimmering in the sunlight pale
Falls each tight-curled golden tail.
The old marshal, dull of wit;
Scratched his head, thought hard on it.
"Nature's wonderful! God's way
Makes us marvel more each day!"
The detachment bowed, much stirred
By the wisdom of his word.
So the marshal made his plans,
Gave the following commands;
Not to buy the steeds or shout,
Not to push or stand about,
That the steeds stay where they are
While he rides to tell the Tzar.
Posting guards, he rode to court
To deliver his report.

Once at court, he makes this plea.
"Mercy, Father-Majesty!"

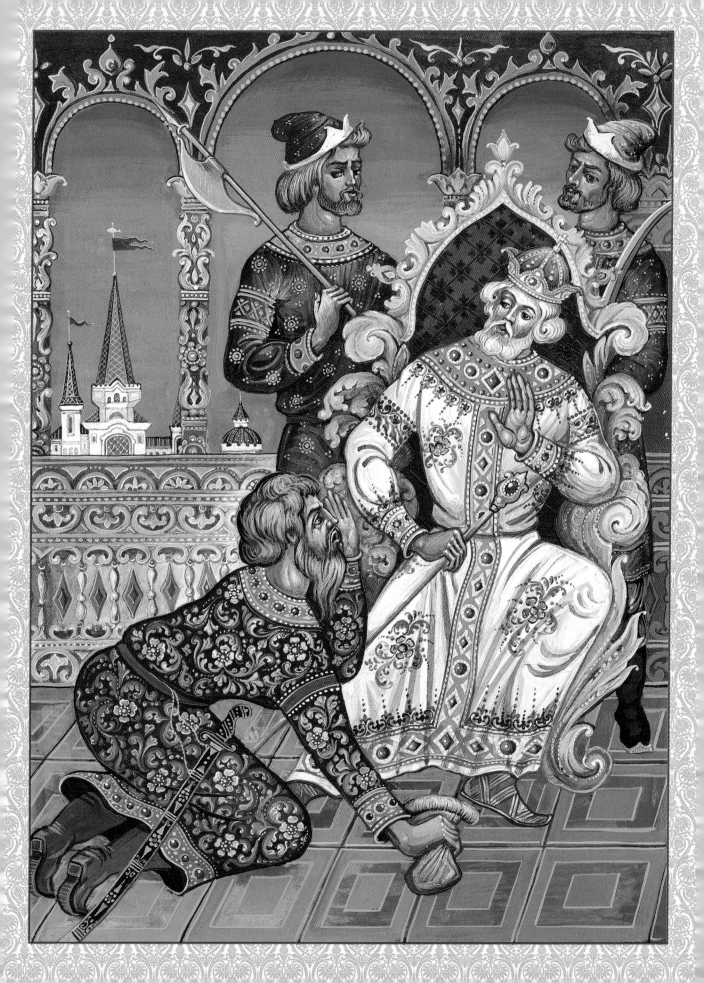

For the moment speaks no more
But falls prostrate on the floor.
Then he says, "Please spare my head.
Bid me speak to you instead."
And the Tzar lifts his suspense.
"Speak, but speak so it makes sense."
"Yes, your Majesty, I'll try.
As your provost-marshal, I
Always do my best. Just so."
"Yes," the Tzar said. "Yes, I know!"
"So my guard and I today
To the horse sales made our way.
There we see an awful crush
Where the people mill and push.
As was proper, I commanded
That the people be disbanded.
So at last, dear Father Tzar,
I moved forward and I saw
To my wonder that a pair
Of breath-taking steeds stood there.
Young, black as the raven's wing,
To each neck gold ringlets cling,
Shimmering in the sunlight pale

Falls each tight-curled golden tail.
Round each diamond hoof is set,
Matched and large, a pearl circlet."

And the Tzar could hardly stay
His impatience. "On our way!
And it wouldn't hurt to buy
Such a wonder," did he cry.
"Fetch the carriage!" One wink late
Stood the carriage at his gate.
First the Tzar dressed, washed his face,
Then drove to the market place
With his large armed archer-forces.

When he drives up to the horses,
On their knees the people fall
And "Hurrah!"in chorus call.
So the old Tzar bows and sweeps,
Lightly from the carriage leaps.
On the steeds he glues his sight;
Walks around their left, their right;
Softly murmuring, with them chats;
Smooths their backs with gentle pats;

Strokes each arching neck again;
Gently pulls each golden mane.
When at last he'd looked his fill,
He turned round and shouted shrill
To the gathered crowd. "Hey, there!
Who's the owner of this pair?
And where is he?" John advanced,
Arms akimbo; almost pranced
From behind his brothers; pride
Swelling in his breast, replied,
"Tzar, this pair belongs to me.
I'm their owner. I am he."
"Well, I'll buy," the old Tzar said.
"Will you sell?" "I'll trade instead."
"Say for what." "Five caps times two,
Silver filled by you, would do."
"That would be ten caps you need."
So they're weighed and paid with speed.
And the Tzar was glad to slip
In five dollars for a tip,
For that Tzar was generous-hearted.
With the steeds stableward started
Ten smart grooms, with silvered locks,

42

Dressed in gold-embroidered smocks,
Varicolored belts, and whips
Of morocco at their hips.
On the way the horses broke
From the hostelers. What a joke!
Tore their reins to shreds to run
Back unto their master, John.

So the Tzar returned—no other
Course remained-and said, "Well, brother,
Our grooms can't control the pair.
Thc solution comes to where
You will work at court in dress,
Gold-embroidered silk, no less,
Scarlet-hued, the eye to please.
Life will be a life of ease,
And I'll put you in full charge
Of my stable grand and large.
The Tzar always keeps his word.
Is't agreed?" "I've rightly heard
That I'll work at court in dress,
Gold-embroidered silk, no less,
Scarlet-hued, the eye to please.

Life will be a life of ease.
That the Tzar puts me in charge
Of his stable grand and large.
I, a yokel, will in short
Bea governor at court.
Wonderful! Agreed! I'll go
Serve you, Tzar, as best I know.
Only mind, don't nag or fight.
Let me get my sleep each night,
Or I'll up and leave the place."

At his call the racers pace
Near him as he walks the streets,
Waves his sleeve, the people greets.
While he sings the horses prance,
Even break into a dance;
And the pony flaunts his pep,
By a gay knee-bending step
Stuns the watching populace.

While John's brothers, in their place,
Took the money the Tzar dealt,
Sewed it firmly in their belt,

45

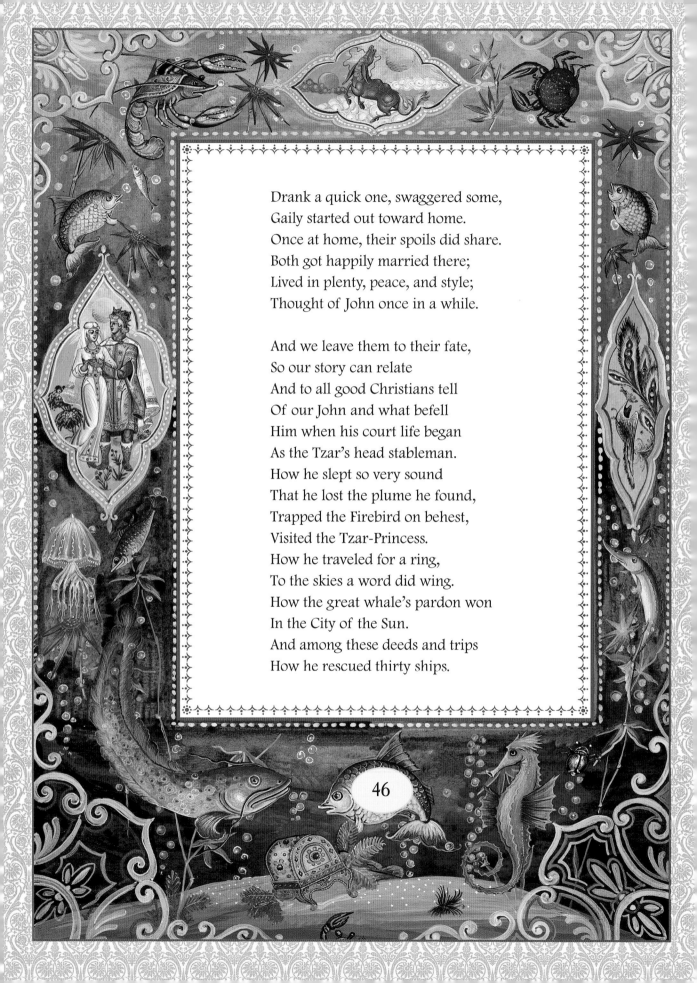

Drank a quick one, swaggered some,
Gaily started out toward home.
Once at home, their spoils did share.
Both got happily married there;
Lived in plenty, peace, and style;
Thought of John once in a while.

And we leave them to their fate,
So our story can relate
And to all good Christians tell
Of our John and what befell
Him when his court life began
As the Tzar's head stableman.
How he slept so very sound
That he lost the plume he found,
Trapped the Firebird on behest,
Visited the Tzar-Princess.
How he traveled for a ring,
To the skies a word did wing.
How the great whale's pardon won
In the City of the Sun.
And among these deeds and trips
How he rescued thirty ships.

In hot caldrons boiled he not,
But grew handsome, too. And, what
Most concerns us near and far,
How he then became the Tzar.

Part II

Tales are easy to be spun,
Deeds are not so quickly done.

But our tale becomes waylaid
Of our John's own escapade
If we think of tales unborn:
Of a gray-brown leprechaun;
Or of goats that seaward wander;
Or of mountains thick with timber;
Of a steed, his gold rein torn,
Rising toward the sun at morn;
Of a still wood that stands proud—
O'er it hangs a thundercloud
(As the cloud moves, lightning breaks
And the sky with thunder shakes).
That's the prologue. Patient be
While the tale spins merrily:
How beyond the boundless sea,
On an isle of mystery,

51

In a wood a bier new-made
Stands. In it a maid is laid.
Sings the nightingale beside it,
Roots the beast in gloom that hides it.
That's a prologue too, but hold!
Soon the story will be told.

So you see, earth-bounded friends,
Upright, worthy, Christian men,
That our hero, a good sort,
Made himself a place at court
In the stables of the Tzar.
And few thoughts his pleasures mar
Of his brothers or his father.
And, in truth, why should he bother,
When his wardrobe—silk, no less—
Is complete with scarlet dress,
Crimson hats, red shoes galore
(He could fill ten trunks or more).
When he eats and sleeps his fill?
Life seems perfect there until...
Five weeks pass. Observes the Knight
Of the Bedchamber—who might

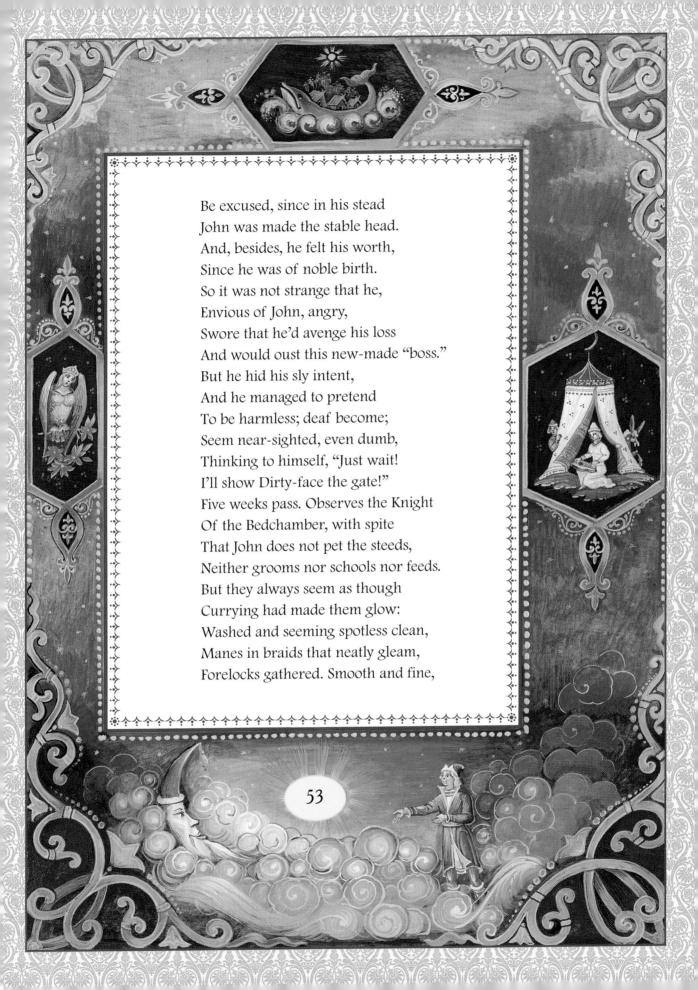

Be excused, since in his stead
John was made the stable head.
And, besides, he felt his worth,
Since he was of noble birth.
So it was not strange that he,
Envious of John, angry,
Swore that he'd avenge his loss
And would oust this new-made "boss."
But he hid his sly intent,
And he managed to pretend
To be harmless; deaf become;
Seem near-sighted, even dumb,
Thinking to himself, "Just wait!
I'll show Dirty-face the gate!"
Five weeks pass. Observes the Knight
Of the Bedchamber, with spite
That John does not pet the steeds,
Neither grooms nor schools nor feeds.
But they always seem as though
Currying had made them glow:
Washed and seeming spotless clean,
Manes in braids that neatly gleam,
Forelocks gathered. Smooth and fine,

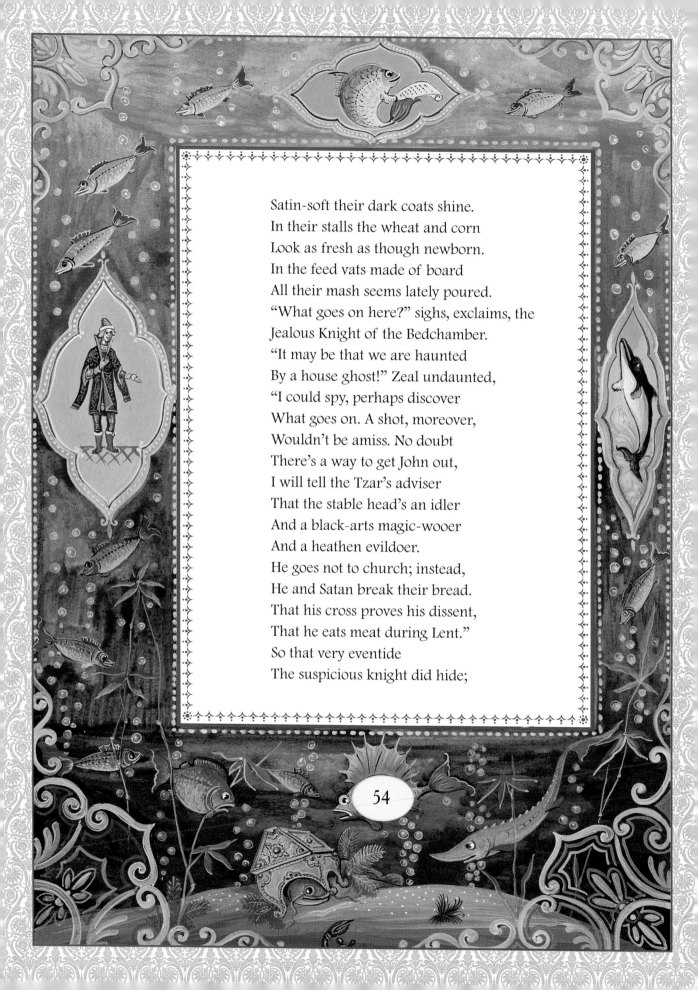

Satin-soft their dark coats shine.
In their stalls the wheat and corn
Look as fresh as though newborn.
In the feed vats made of board
All their mash seems lately poured.
"What goes on here?" sighs, exclaims, the
Jealous Knight of the Bedchamber.
"It may be that we are haunted
By a house ghost!" Zeal undaunted,
"I could spy, perhaps discover
What goes on. A shot, moreover,
Wouldn't be amiss. No doubt
There's a way to get John out,
I will tell the Tzar's adviser
That the stable head's an idler
And a black-arts magic-wooer
And a heathen evildoer.
He goes not to church; instead,
He and Satan break their bread.
That his cross proves his dissent,
That he eats meat during Lent."
So that very eventide
The suspicious knight did hide;

54

On the stable floor he lay
Neatly hidden in the hay.

Midnight came. Fright seemed to press
Out the bravery in his breast,
And he lay, less live than dead,
While a prayer ran through his head,
Waiting. Suddenly a slight
Creak of doors disturbed the night;
And the steeds' stamp heralded
The arriving stable head,
Who came in and barred the door,
Carefully doffed the hat he wore,
Laid it on the window ledge
And took out of it a wedge.
In it, wrapped with rags together,
Lay the treasured Firebird's feather.
And so blinding shone its light
That the knight scarce stilled his fright,
And he shook so, where he lay,
He shook off the covering hay.
But the villain, blind to danger,
Puts the feather in a manger

And begins to groom a steed:
Washes, rubs, with practiced speed,
Braids the mane that falls so long,
Singing many a different song.
Meanwhile, in a hall rolled tight,
His teeth chattering with fright,
The knight, half-alive at most,
Notes the doings of this ghost.
An odd demon! Still; who knows
Why he prowls in such fine clothes?
He has neither horns nor beard;
He looks handsome and not weird.
Smooth, his hair; ribboned, his side;
Fancy galloons his shirt dandified;
Scarlet, soft, morocco shoes—
Fine a gent as one could choose!
What a wonder! One more look
At the ghost the watcher took.
"This is what I'll plan," the sly
Meddler grumbled. "For will I
To the Tzar next day reveal,
What you, stupid, would conceal.
Wait a day; you'll have, you'll see,

Reason to remember me!"
And our John, all ignorant
Of the troubles that portend,
Braids the flowing golden manes,
Singing various tuneful strains.
Having currycombed each steed,
Into vats strained honeyed feed,
Filled the full vats fuller yet
With the finest, purest millet.
He then yawned and hid the feather;
Wrapped up with the rags together,
In his cap beneath his head,
Near the hind feet made his bed.

When the dawn began to break,
Then the knight stirred. Wide-awake,
Listened till a lusty snore
Told him John would sleep some more.
Then he left his hiding place;
Crawling, reached beneath John's face;
Slipped his fingers in John's hat;
Grabbed the feather; fled at that.
Hardly had the Tzar awoken

When the knight came with his token.
To the floor he bowed his head,
Singsonging, the following said:
"With a guilty head, O Tzar,
Do I come to where you are.
But have mercy, spare my head,
Bid me speak to you instead."
"Speak without exaggeration,"
Yawned the Tzar without elation.
"If you speak with lying lip,
You will not escape the whip."
So the knight gathered his strength,
Managed to reply at length:
"It's God's truth, is my report;
I've not tried, Tzar, to distort.
We all know John does a wrong,
Hides what to you should belong.
Neither gold nor silver treasure,
Firebird's feather, is his pleasure."
"Firebird's feather! Does he dare
To so fill his purse? Beware.
Wait, you evildoer. Do.
I'll not spare the whips on you."

"And he knows still more, does John,"
Quietly the knight tells on,
Still bent double. "Speak of treasure,
Let him keep that plume for pleasure.
But he brags that he could bring,
Should you ask of him this thing,
To your city, Father, pray,
A whole Firebird any day."
The accuser stopped to stoop
In a bow round as a hoop,
Bore the treasure to the bed,
To the floor then bent his head.

And the Tzar with spellbound look
Stroked his beard, with laughter shook,
Bit the feather's tip, thought best
Then to lay it in a chest.
After this, impatient, shrill,
Made he known his royal will
With a quick wave of his wrist—
"Bring John here!"and thumped his fist.
And the couriers, rich and grand,
Sped to do the Tzar's command

But, converging near the door,
Bumped each other to the floor.
And the Tzar watched their mistake,
Laughed until his sides did ache.
When they noticed that the Tzar
Thought this funny, from afar
Quick they glanced at one another
And again tripped up each other.
And the Tzar was pleased and willed
That a hat be silver-filled.
After this the nobles went,
On their quest for John intent;
Feeling sobered, did not mix
Themselves up in further tricks.

When they reach the stableyard
They go in, leave doors unbarred.
With their feet they prod at John,
At his sides and up and down.
Half an hour they try to wake him,
But he cares not how they shake him.
Then at last a passing groom
Wakes him poking with his broom.

"And what menials have we here?"
Said John, rising with a mere
"If I take the whip to you
You'll remember well not to
Wake John up if 'tis for naught."
Spoke the nobles, "We have brought
Orders from the Tzar that we
Fetch you to him speedily."
"Oh, the Tzar? I guess I'd best
Dress and answer his behest."
Thusly, then, replied our John,
And he put his shirtwaist on,
Tied his fancy belt in place,
Brushed his hair and washed his face,
Buckled on his whip. And pride
Made his gait a swanlike glide.

So before the Tzar came John;
Bowed, his courage called upon;
Cleared his throat twice and demanded,
"You to rouse me have commanded?"
And the Tzar, his left eye squinting,
Shouted, with his anger glinting,

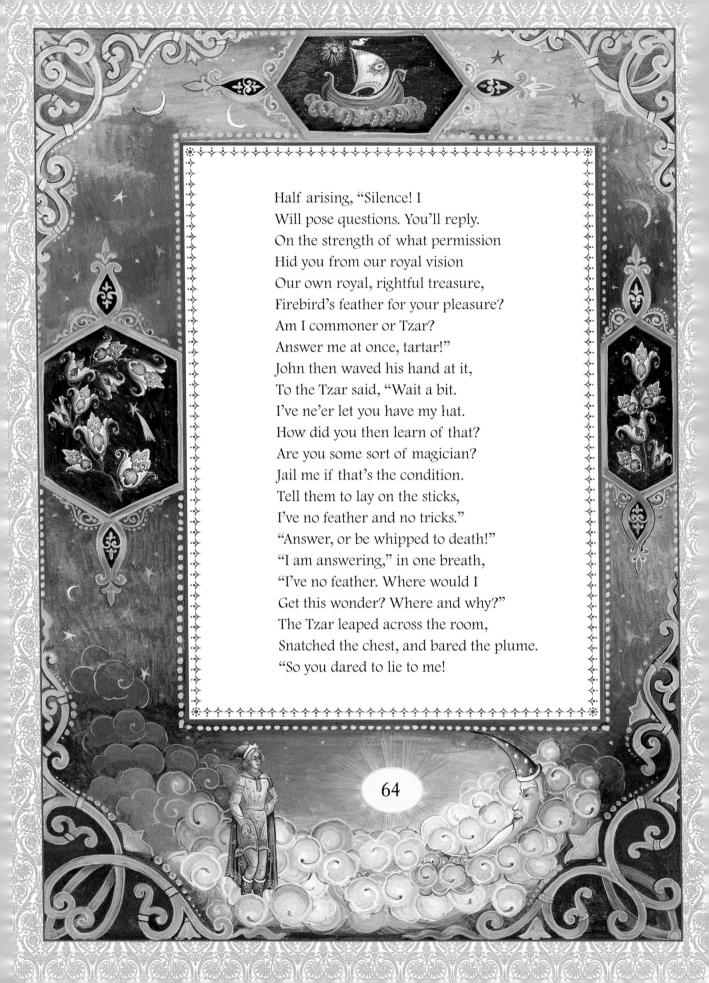

Half arising, "Silence! I
Will pose questions. You'll reply.
On the strength of what permission
Hid you from our royal vision
Our own royal, rightful treasure,
Firebird's feather for your pleasure?
Am I commoner or Tzar?
Answer me at once, tartar!"
John then waved his hand at it,
To the Tzar said, "Wait a bit.
I've ne'er let you have my hat.
How did you then learn of that?
Are you some sort of magician?
Jail me if that's the condition.
Tell them to lay on the sticks,
I've no feather and no tricks."
"Answer, or be whipped to death!"
"I am answering," in one breath,
"I've no feather. Where would I
Get this wonder? Where and why?"
The Tzar leaped across the room,
Snatched the chest, and bared the plume.
"So you dared to lie to me!

It's too late to wiggle free.
What lies here, eh?"And our John
Shook as leaf shakes in a storm,
Even dropped his hat from fright.
"Well, my friend, the spot is tight,"
Spoke the Tzar. "Wait, brother. Halt."
"Oh, forgive me! I'm at fault.
Pardon John, who owns his blame,
And he'll never lie again,"
John pled, and then spoke no more
But fell prostrate on the floor.
"Well, be pardoned since this be
The first time you've lied to me,"
Said the Tzar to John. "I'm still
Angry, Lord forgive, and will,
Should you give me cause—take care—
Lift your scalp off by the hair.
Now, you know how I can rail.
So, without too much detail,
You have bragged, or so I heard,
You could fetch the Firebird
To our city, should you wish.
So take care, and don't deny it,

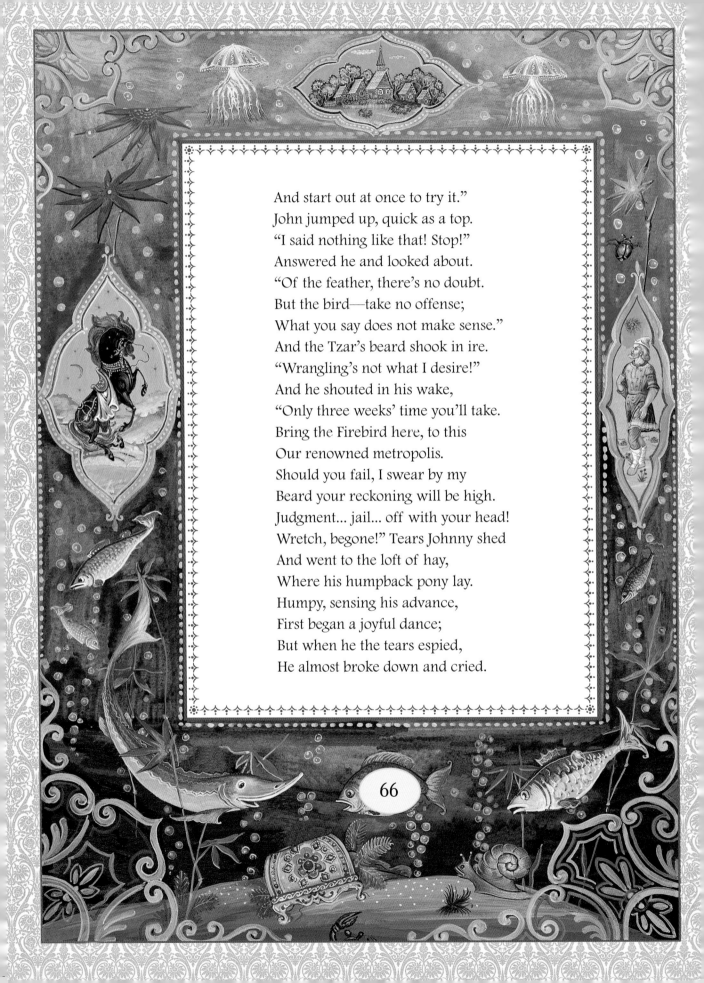

And start out at once to try it."
John jumped up, quick as a top.
"I said nothing like that! Stop!"
Answered he and looked about.
"Of the feather, there's no doubt.
But the bird—take no offense;
What you say does not make sense."
And the Tzar's beard shook in ire.
"Wrangling's not what I desire!"
And he shouted in his wake,
"Only three weeks' time you'll take.
Bring the Firebird here, to this
Our renowned metropolis.
Should you fail, I swear by my
Beard your reckoning will be high.
Judgment... jail... off with your head!
Wretch, begone!" Tears Johnny shed
And went to the loft of hay,
Where his humpback pony lay.
Humpy, sensing his advance,
First began a joyful dance;
But when he the tears espied,
He almost broke down and cried.

"Why is Johnny sad?" he pled.
"Why hangs low his bonnie head?"
Gently asked the little horse,
Prancing, restless with remorse.
"Bare your secret first, then start—
Tell me all that's in your heart.
I will help you all I can.
Are you ill, dear friend, kind man?
Does some rogue abuse you? Tell."
Round the pony's neck John fell,
Kissed him, hugged him with full force.
"Woe is me, my little horse.
'Fetch,' so bade the sovereign's word,
'To me here, the Firebird.'
Humpy, tell me what to do."
Spoke the pony, "Though 'tis true
That the trouble's great, I'll find
Ways to help you. Never mind.
All this trouble comes, you see,
From not listening to me.
Traveling capital ward together,
When you found the Firebird's feather,
You remember what I said:

'Leave it; from it trouble's bred,
For you'll find unrest, heartbreak,
Closely follow in its wake.'
Now, too late, you know that I
Spoke the truth, and can see why.
But in friendship let me state
That this favor's small, not great.
The real service lies ahead.
Go you to the Tzar instead.
Tell him frankly then enough,
'Tzar, I needs must have a trough—
Even two –and pure white millet
And imported wine. And still it
Would be best you haste supplies.
Dawns the morrow in the skies,
We depart at break of day.'"
To the Tzar, John makes his way;
Tells him frankly then enough,
"Tzar, I needs must have a trough—
Even two—and pure white millet
And imported wine. And still it
Would be best you haste supplies.
Dawns the morrow in the skies,

68

We depart at break of day."
And the Tzar, without delay,
Orders noble errand men
To fulfill John's needs right then.
Calls him brave and calls him worthy,
Says "Good luck" and "Pleasant journey."

Bright and early in the morning
Humpy woke John with the warning,
"Wake up, master. Cease your dreaming.
Time to start your woes redeeming."
Johnny roused, rose then and there
For the journey to prepare;
Took the millet and the trough
And imported wine; enough
Clothing donned against the cold;
Mounted Humpy as of old;
Found a crust on which to feast;
And departed toward the east,
The rare Firebird for to seek.

So they ride full long a week.
On the eighth day of their quest

They approach a deep forest.
There to John the pony said,
"In the forest is a glade.
Near the glade there is a hill.
Made of silver pure and still.
And 'tis there at break of light
That the Firebirds make their flight
To drink water from the brook.
So 'tis here that we must look."
Having this to John revealed,
Humpy gallops o'er the field.
Such a field! The grass is green
With a precious emerald's sheen.
As the mildest breeze does pass,
Sparks of light fly from the grass.
And among the grass blades grow
Flowers whose beauty words can't show.
What is more—there was revealed,
Like a billow o'er the field,
Rising, a breath-taking hill
Made of silver, pure and still.
And the summer sun's rays fall,
Paint a sunset o'er it all,

In its hollows golden nest,
Burn like candles on its crest.
So the pony slantwise bent
Up this hill in fast ascent.
Climbed five hundred yards this way,
Then stood still to have his say.
"Soon the night will fall, when, John,
You must watch right through till dawn.
First pour in your troughs the wine,
To it add the millet fine.
To be hid, but close enough,
Crawl beneath the other trough.
Then keep silent, watching out,
But have all your wits about.
Here, before the break of light
Will the Firebirds make their flight.
Hungry to the grain they'll fly,
Fill the air with their shrill cry.
Grab the one that's nearest you
By the tail. Watch what you do.
Having caught the bird, then shout
Just as loud as sound will out.
Promptly I'll be there to help."

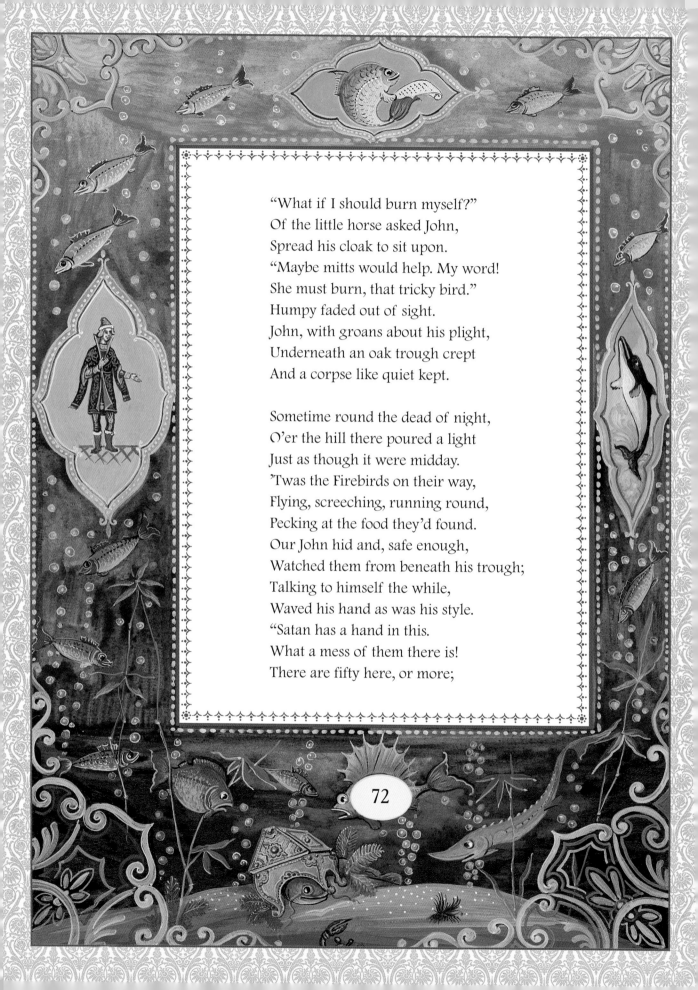

"What if I should burn myself?"
Of the little horse asked John,
Spread his cloak to sit upon.
"Maybe mitts would help. My word!
She must burn, that tricky bird."
Humpy faded out of sight.
John, with groans about his plight,
Underneath an oak trough crept
And a corpse like quiet kept.

Sometime round the dead of night,
O'er the hill there poured a light
Just as though it were midday.
'Twas the Firebirds on their way,
Flying, screeching, running round,
Pecking at the food they'd found.
Our John hid and, safe enough,
Watched them from beneath his trough;
Talking to himself the while,
Waved his hand as was his style.
"Satan has a hand in this.
What a mess of them there is!
There are fifty here, or more;

Nice to catch the whole threescore.
That would make a pretty profit.
And such beauties, too. Think of it!
They've red feet, but that's not half;
And their tails, they'd make you laugh!
Nothing like the ones on chicken.
But the light they throw would sicken
The bright glow in father's stove."
Thus John stopped the speech he wove
To himself. Hid 'neath his cover,
Like a snake he sidled over
To the grain and wine repast;
Grabbed one bird's tail; held it fast.
"Run, my humpy pony! Lend
Me your help, my little friend,
For I've caught the Firebird!"
Shouted John the happy word.
Humpy came in half a trice.
"Well done, master. That was nice!"
Said the little horse. "Now, sir,
Quickly in the sack with her,
And be sure to tie it fast.
Hang it round your neck and, last,

We must homeward on our way."
"Let me shoo the birds first, pray.
Look," said John, the meanwhile reaching,
"They will strain themselves with
                                    screeching,"
For the other gunnysack;
Grabbed it, whipped it round and back.
As a living blaze of fame
Rose the whole flock from the plain,
Curving in a fiery ring
Past the clouds on whirring wing.
While our John stood throwing fits,
Waving at them with his mitts,
Shouting at them with a cry
As though he'd been doused with lye.
With the birds lost in a cloud,
And their treasures packed, the proud
Travelers turned their steps to come
Safely back unto their home.

They arrived. "Well, did you bring
Me the Firebird?" Straight did fling
That demand the Tzar, his sight

Fastened on the tattling knight,
Who stood there and, wrathful, sick,
Bit his nails down to the quick.
"Why, of course, I've got the bird!"
Was our John's triumphant word.
"Then where is it?" "Here, Tzar, but
First give the command to shut
All the shutters in your room
So that you create a gloom."
And the waiting nobles sped,
Closed the shutters as John said.
On a table lay Jonny's sack.
"Out with you, old girl. Unpack!"
Instantly, a flood of light;
Raised their hands to shield their sight.
Cried the Tzar in accents dire,
"Mercy! Save us! We're on fire!
Call the firemen! They ought to
Come to quench it. Water! Water!"
"It's not fire. That blaze so bright
Nothing is but Firebird's light,"
Spoke the tactful one (while he
Nearly burst with stifled glee).

"Tzar, I've brought you novel sport."
And the Tzar made this retort,
"Fond am I of you, friend John.
Light my heart feels from the fun;
Joy reigns. For reward assume
The new post of Tzar's own groom."
Hearing this, the cunning Knight
Of the Bedchamber, his spite
Unappeased, spoke 'neath his nose,
"Wait, you suckling. In the throes
Of the future lies your due.
Satan's luck won't be with you
Next time, for I'll not remain
Beaten, but will try again."

Three weeks after this there sat
Of an evening for a chat,
In the palace kitchen quarters,
Chefs, domestics, palace porters,
Drinking jugs of honey mead
While a wonder-tale they read.
When a flunky murmured, "What
A fine wonder-book I've got,

Lent me by a friend today!
Few its pages, I must say,
And the tales are only five.
But what tales! Why, they contrive
To entrance you to the last."
Begged the listeners in a chorus,
"Tell the story! Tell it for us!"
"Gladly, if it will amuse.
There are five from which to choose.
First there was a 'Beaver Story';
Next a tale of 'Tzar and Glory';
Third, if memory has not ceased,
Of a 'Peeress of the East';
Fourth, told of a 'Lonely Prince';
And the fifth—a second since
It was running through my head.
I forget the fifth, it read—"
"Well, let's let it go. But hold!
Of a beauty was it told?"
"Yes. Exactly. Nothing less.
It tells of the 'Tzar-Princess.'
Which of these, my good friends, pray,
Would you have me tell today?"

"Tell us of the Tzar-Princess!"
Rose the shout. "Of kings, we guess,
We've heard often. Tell the one
Of the beauty. It's more fun!"
And the flunky sat in state,
Slowly did his tale relate.
"Near the distant, unknown land
Lies a sea, friends. Understand
That the men who sail that sea
Are all heathens. Such as we
From this Christian land ne'er went,
Nobles, commoners, ne'er spent
Time nor money nor emotion,
On that far, polluted ocean.
'Tis from merchants that we hear
Of a maiden, just by ear,
A rare maiden on that water;
For she is the Moon's own daughter,
And her brother is the Sun.
And this maid, the tale does run,
In a crimson short fur coat,
Sails a little golden boat.
When she rows her boat—what's more—

80

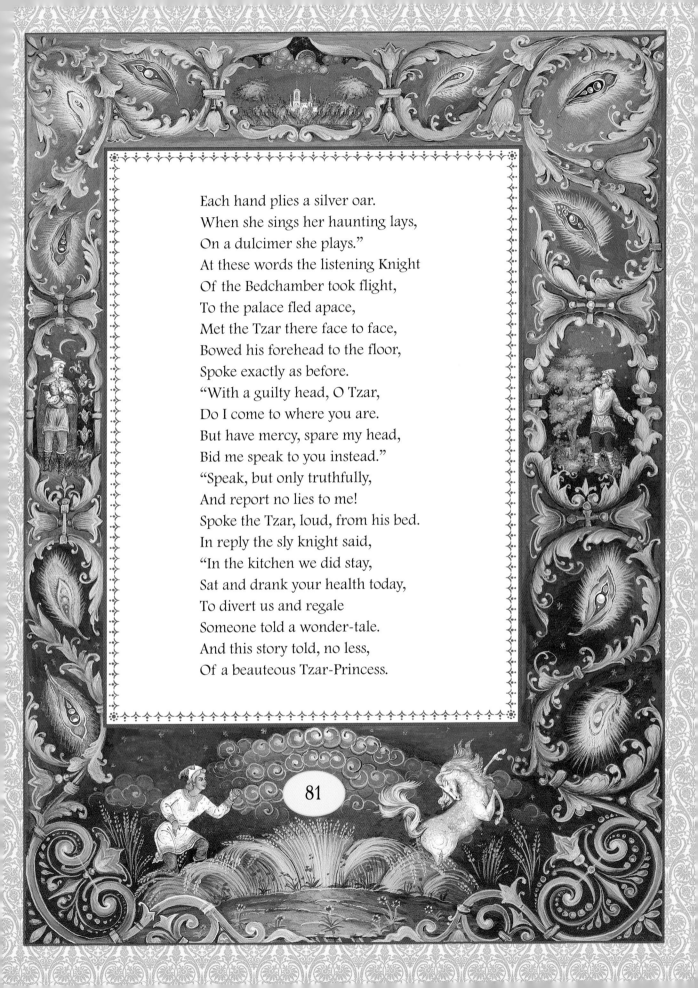

Each hand plies a silver oar.
When she sings her haunting lays,
On a dulcimer she plays."
At these words the listening Knight
Of the Bedchamber took flight,
To the palace fled apace,
Met the Tzar there face to face,
Bowed his forehead to the floor,
Spoke exactly as before.
"With a guilty head, O Tzar,
Do I come to where you are.
But have mercy, spare my head,
Bid me speak to you instead."
"Speak, but only truthfully,
And report no lies to me!
Spoke the Tzar, loud, from his bed.
In reply the sly knight said,
"In the kitchen we did stay,
Sat and drank your health today,
To divert us and regale
Someone told a wonder-tale.
And this story told, no less,
Of a beauteous Tzar-Princess.

And your personal groom did swear,
By the royal beard you wear,
That he knows this 'tricky bird'
For the Tzar-Princess, his word.
And I bring this to your ear,
Brags that he could bring her here."
And the knight bowed to the floor,
"Bring the groom!" the Tzar did roar
To his messengers. The knight
Stepped behind and out of sight.
And the couriers, rich and grand,
Sped to do the Tsar's command,
Found John fast asleep and curt,
Brought him in his sleeping shirt.
And the Tzar this speech began:
"Johnny, I've been told, my man,
That you bragged that you could bring
To us here this wondrous thing,
This 'unusual bird'—confess—
Known and called the Tzar-Princess."
"Why, that's nonsense" to the room
In reply began the groom.
"I'm still half asleep; you pick

A queer time to play a trick.
Joke. Be cunning. Test your wit.
You won't fool me—not a bit."
Now the Tzar's beard shook in ire.
"Wrangling's not what I desire."
And he shouted in his wake,
"Only three weeks' time you'll take.
Bring the Tzar-Princess to this
Our renowned metropolis.
Should you fail, I swear by my
Beard your reckoning will be high.
Judgment... jail... off with your head!
Wretch, begone!" Tears Johnny shed
And went to the loft of hay,
Where his humpback pony lay.

"Why is Johnny sad?" he pled.
"Why hangs low his bonnie head?"
Gently asked the little horse.
"Are you feeling ill? Or, worse,
Does some rogue abuse you? Tell."
Round the pony's neck John fell,
Kissed him, hugged him with full force.

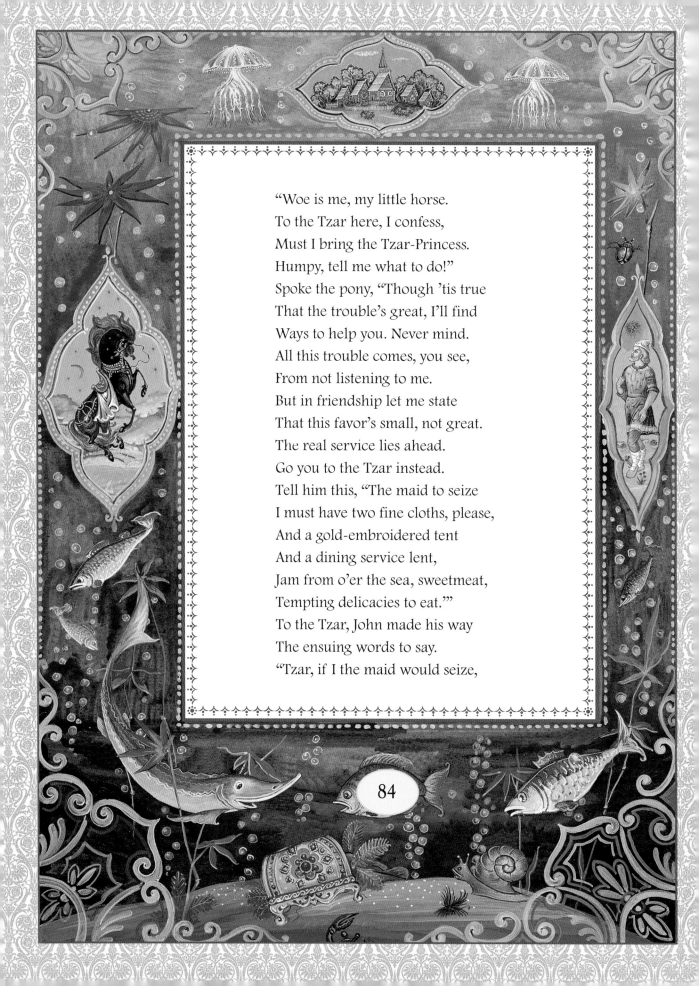

"Woe is me, my little horse.
To the Tzar here, I confess,
Must I bring the Tzar-Princess.
Humpy, tell me what to do!"
Spoke the pony, "Though 'tis true
That the trouble's great, I'll find
Ways to help you. Never mind.
All this trouble comes, you see,
From not listening to me.
But in friendship let me state
That this favor's small, not great.
The real service lies ahead.
Go you to the Tzar instead.
Tell him this, "The maid to seize
I must have two fine cloths, please,
And a gold-embroidered tent
And a dining service lent,
Jam from o'er the sea, sweetmeat,
Tempting delicacies to eat.'"
To the Tzar, John made his way
The ensuing words to say.
"Tzar, if I the maid would seize,

84

I must have two fine cloths, please,
And a gold-embroidered tent
And a dining service lent,
Jam from o'er the sea, sweetmeat,
Tempting delicacies to eat."
"Why spoke you not so straightway?"
From his bed the Tzar did say,
Told his noble errand men
To fulfill John's orders then.
Called him brave and called him worthy,
Said "Good luck" and "Pleasant journey."
Bright and early in the morning
Humpy woke John with the warning,
"Wake up, master. Cease your dreaming.
Time to start your woes redeeming."
Johnny roused, rose then and there
For the journey to prepare;
Took the two fine cloths and tent
And the service that was lent
And the jam from overseas
And the sweets and delicacies;
Packed them in his traveling kit,

Tied a rope round all of it;
Warmly dressed against the cold,
Mounted Humpy as of old,
Found a crust on which to feast;
And departed toward the east,
The Tzar-Princess for to seek.

So they ride full long a week.
On the eighth day of their quest
They approach a deep forest.
There the pony spoke to John.
"Here's the roadway to the ocean,
Where the beauty all year round
Lives; and there she can be found.
Twice on land she does appear;
Brings the long day of the year
To our earth, as you will see
On the morrow presently."
Having this to John described,
Gallops to the oceanside,
Where, white-crested, one wave keeps
Wandering lonely o'er the deeps.

And, dismounting from the horse,
John gives heed to his discourse.
"Pitch the tent," the pony said.
"Lay the cloth. The service spread.
Serve the jam from overseas.
And the sweets and delicacies.
Then behind the tent hide out,
But keep all your wits about.
See a twinkling toward us float?
That's the Princess' little boat.
Let her come into the tent.
Let her feast till she's content.
When she's finished, quickly run
In the tent. Seize her. Hold on,
But be careful to hold tight.
Call for me with all your might.
At your very first command
I'll appear and be on hand
To ride home. But cautious be;
Watch her closely, prudently.
If you miss this chance you've got,
Miserable will be your lot."

Disappeared the little horse.
John, back of the tent, of course,
Strove to bore a little slit
To peep at the maid through it.
Clear the midday comes, and more.
Lands the Princess on the shore;
Takes her dulcimer to the tent;
Seats herself, on feasting bent.
"So this is the Tzar-Princess,
Who the wonder-tales profess,"
Johnny murmurs, "has such grace
And such beauty, and a face,
That's so marvelously fair.
I can see no beauty here.
She is pale and thin beside,
Her waist's not five inches wide.
And her foot, thin as a peg—
It looks like a chicken's leg!
Welcome, he who wants this beauty;
I'd not take her, free of duty."
Softly does the Princess play,
Sweetly sings a gentle lay.

And our John is charmed by this;
Listens, lying on his fist,
While the voice melodious keeps
Lulling him until he sleeps.
Day was dying in the west.
Neighed the pony o'er his breast,
Prodded at him with his hoof,
Shouted in enraged reproof.
"Sleep till shines the evening star!
Sleep till woe your sleep will mar!
It's not I who'll lose my head."
Then our Johnny wept and pled;
Weeping, begged in deep remorse
Pardon of the little horse.
Please forgive John for his sin.
I'll not fall asleep again."
"Heaven grant you be reprieved!"
Humpy shouted, still aggrieved.
"But, remember, should we fix
This, that sleep and work don't mix!
With tomorrow morn's advent,
To the gold-embroidered tent
The Princess will come to savor

Once again the mead's fine flavor.
If to sleep this time you choose,
Count your head lost in a noose."

Humpy vanished with these words.
Johnny piled up stones and boards;
Nails from sides, bottoms, and decks
Of some beached old sailing wrecks,
So they'd stick him and awake him
Should a drowsiness o'ertake him.

Early on the morn's advent,
To the gold-embroidered tent
Sails the Tzar-Princess once more;
Pulls her boat upon the shore;
Takes her dulcimer to the tent;
Seats herself, on feasting bent.
Softly does the Princess play,
Sweetly sings a gentle lay.
And again our John does keep
Feeling that he wants to sleep.
"Not again, you little cheat,"
Says John, rising to his feet,

92

"Will you get away, not twice
Will I fall for this device."
Fast into the tent runs John,
Grabs her long braids and hangs on.
"Come, my little horse! Run fast.
Help me. I've caught her at last."
Humpy comes in half a trice.
"Well done, master. That was nice!
Now move quickly, and climb on;
Hold on to her tightly, John!"

They reach the metropolis.
Runs the Tzar to the Princess,
Takes her dainty, pale white hand,
Leads her to the palace grand,
Begs her grace his oaken table
Overhung with silks. Scarce able
To contain his love, he tries
To look deep into her eyes.
Maid, whose beauty is supreme,
Reassure me. Be my queen.
Once I saw you—heed my plea—
Fresh my ardor flamed in me.

93

As the falcon's, your proud eye
Makes me nightly sleepless lie.
With the morn comes no respite;
It torments me day and night.
Speak the tender word, for," said he,
"The whole wedding feast is ready.
In the morning, loved one, we
Shall be wed, and happily
Will we live and thrive and laugh."
But the Princess, silent, half
Listening, turned away her head,
Spurned the Tzar and what he said.
Still the Tzar, unangered, strove
Further, falling more in love;
Stood before her on his knee,
Held her hands most tenderly,
And began to bleat again.
"Speak the tender word." And then,
"Are you hurt? I spoke too soon?
Is my love inopportune?"
"Sad my fate is, I confess,"
Spoke in answer the Princess.
"If you wish to have me, sire,

94

Fetch in three days my desire
From the sea—my finger ring."
"Fetch me John to do this thing!"
And the Tzar scarce still could stand
While they ran at his command.

So before the Tzar comes John.
And the Tzar so calls upon
And appeals to him: "For me
Take a trip, John, to the sea,
From whose depths I bid you bring
The Princess' finger ring.
Do this and 'twill be my pleasure
Just to shower you with treasure."
"I can hardly move about
Since the first time I went out,
Now again 'Go to the sea!'"
John replied aggrievedly.
"Knave, how dare you not proceed
When I would my wedding speed!'
Shouts the Tzar in anger's heat,
Stamping his impatient feet.
"Don't stand there recanting, dunce.
Start the journeying at once!"

96

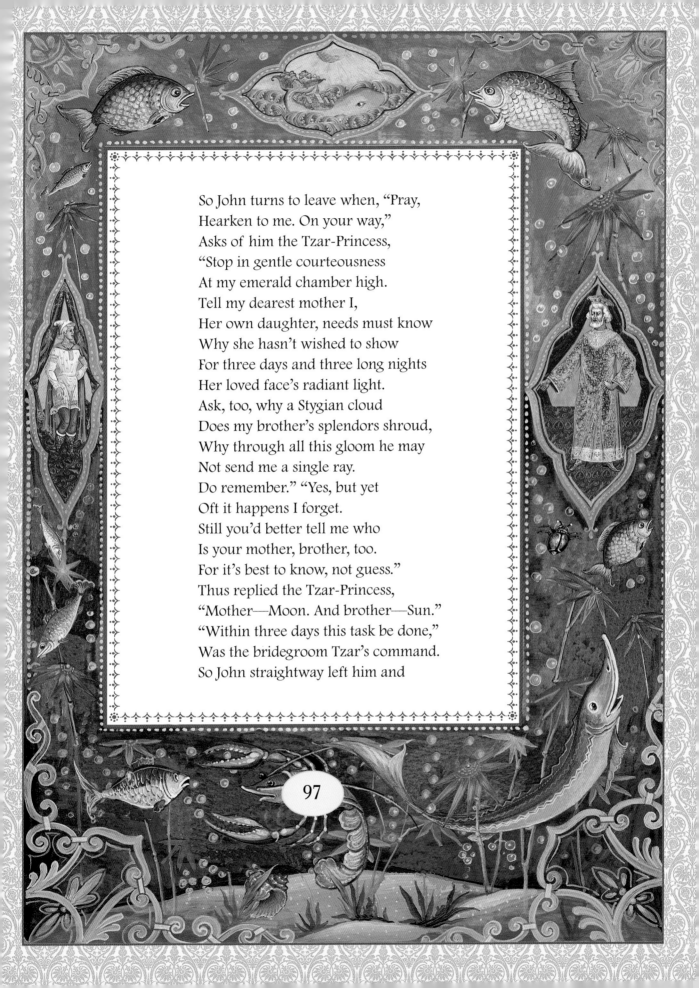

So John turns to leave when, "Pray,
Hearken to me. On your way,"
Asks of him the Tzar-Princess,
"Stop in gentle courteousness
At my emerald chamber high.
Tell my dearest mother I,
Her own daughter, needs must know
Why she hasn't wished to show
For three days and three long nights
Her loved face's radiant light.
Ask, too, why a Stygian cloud
Does my brother's splendors shroud,
Why through all this gloom he may
Not send me a single ray.
Do remember." "Yes, but yet
Oft it happens I forget.
Still you'd better tell me who
Is your mother, brother, too.
For it's best to know, not guess."
Thus replied the Tzar-Princess,
"Mother—Moon. And brother—Sun."
"Within three days this task be done,"
Was the bridegroom Tzar's command.
So John straightway left him and

Went up to the loft of hay,
Where his humpback pony lay.

"Why is Johnny sad?" he pled.
"Why hangs low his bonnie head?"
Gently asked the little horse.
"Help me, Humpy. It, of course,
Is the Tzar's desire that he
Wed the Princess from o'ersea.
So he sends me to the ocean,"
Answered Johnny with emotion.
"Gave me but three days to try
To find where in it does lie,
And then fetch some cursed ring!
And that Princess, poor thin thing,
Bade me at some chamber high
Pay a visit in the sky
To the Sun and Moon, and bear
Messages to them up there."
Spoke the pony, "Let me state
That this favor's small, not great.
The real service lies ahead.
It is best you go to bed,

For at break of dawn we'll be
Swiftly traveling to the sea."

On the morrow John did pack
Three small onions in his sack;
Warmly dressed against the cold,
Mounted Humpy as of old;
And departed on his quest....
Friends, I'm weary, let me rest!

Part III

*Makar used to work and bow,
Look, he is a voivode now.*

102

From the paddock, fa-la-la
Broke the chargers, tra-la-la.
Soon the clever peasant men
Caught and tied them fast again.
Sits a raven on an oak
Toots a horn with every croak;
And his tooting tales and grace
Please the listening populace.
"Hearken while I tell a tale
Of a wife and husband hale.
He was fond of jokes and playing,
And his wife of adage saying.
There such revelries abound
That they're heard the world round."
That's a prologue still, but hold!
Soon our story will be told.

103

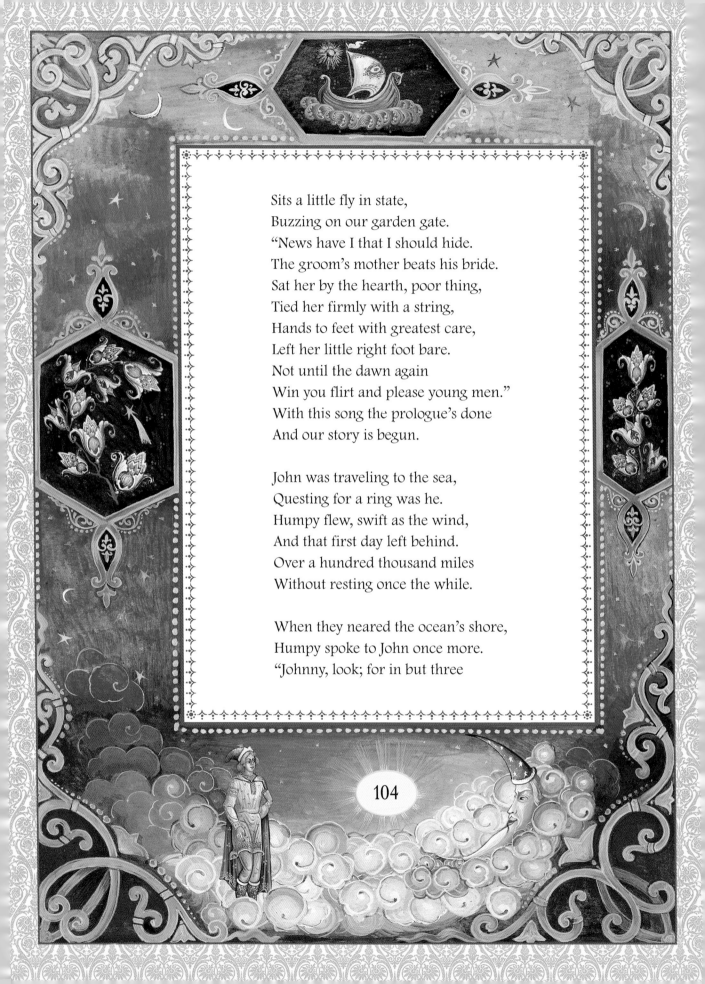

Sits a little fly in state,
Buzzing on our garden gate.
"News have I that I should hide.
The groom's mother beats his bride.
Sat her by the hearth, poor thing,
Tied her firmly with a string,
Hands to feet with greatest care,
Left her little right foot bare.
Not until the dawn again
Win you flirt and please young men."
With this song the prologue's done
And our story is begun.

John was traveling to the sea,
Questing for a ring was he.
Humpy flew, swift as the wind,
And that first day left behind.
Over a hundred thousand miles
Without resting once the while.

When they neared the ocean's shore,
Humpy spoke to John once more.
"Johnny, look; for in but three

Moments we will reach the sea,
Come out on a tableland
Running wide along the strand.
There, upon the beach impaled,
Lies the Wonder-Monster whale;
Ten long years in grief and pain
Yearns for pardon, but in vain,
And atones for some transgression.
He will beg your intercession
That forgiveness might be won
In the City of the Sun.
Promise to fulfill this mission
And remember his commission."
They emerge upon the strand
By the sea, of tableland,
Where, upon the beach impaled,
Lies the Wonder-Monster whale.
Pitted are his sides, stockades,
Fences on his ribs are raised.
On his tail a woodland's grown.
On his back there stands a town.
On his lip the peasants plow.
Striplings dance upon his brow.

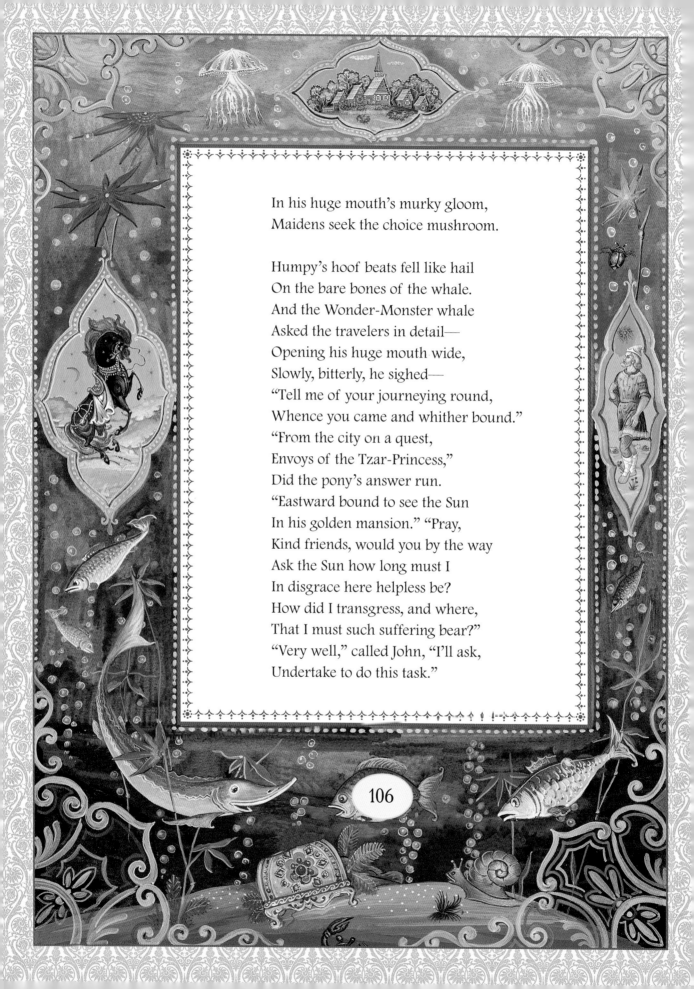

In his huge mouth's murky gloom,
Maidens seek the choice mushroom.

Humpy's hoof beats fell like hail
On the bare bones of the whale.
And the Wonder-Monster whale
Asked the travelers in detail—
Opening his huge mouth wide,
Slowly, bitterly, he sighed—
"Tell me of your journeying round,
Whence you came and whither bound."
"From the city on a quest,
Envoys of the Tzar-Princess,"
Did the pony's answer run.
"Eastward bound to see the Sun
In his golden mansion." "Pray,
Kind friends, would you by the way
Ask the Sun how long must I
In disgrace here helpless be?
How did I transgress, and where,
That I must such suffering bear?"
"Very well," called John, "I'll ask,
Undertake to do this task."

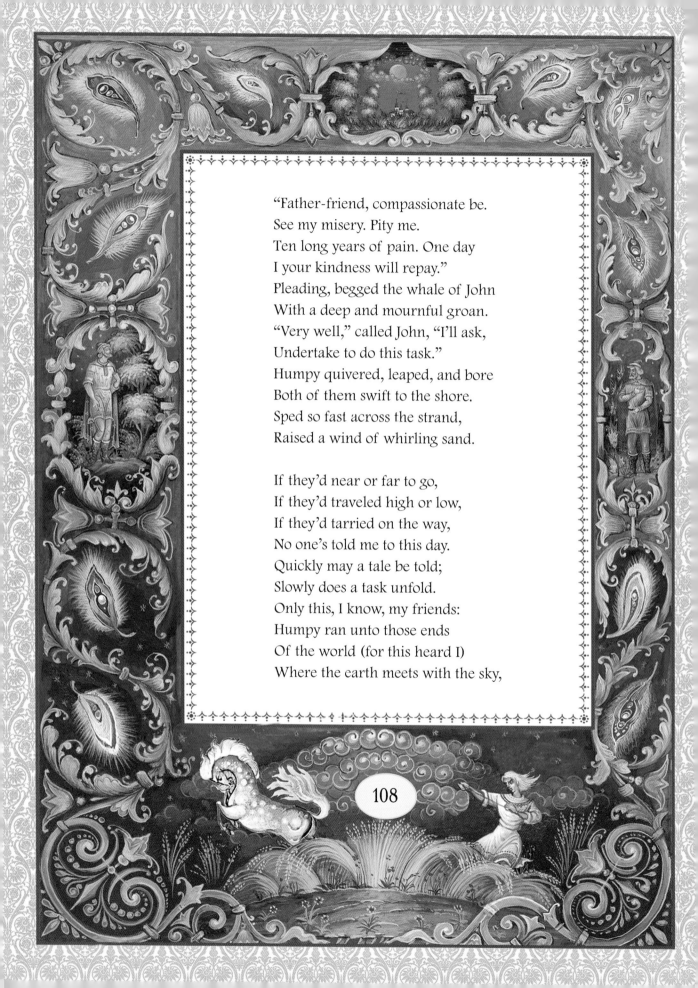

"Father-friend, compassionate be.
See my misery. Pity me.
Ten long years of pain. One day
I your kindness will repay."
Pleading, begged the whale of John
With a deep and mournful groan.
"Very well," called John, "I'll ask,
Undertake to do this task."
Humpy quivered, leaped, and bore
Both of them swift to the shore.
Sped so fast across the strand,
Raised a wind of whirling sand.

If they'd near or far to go,
If they'd traveled high or low,
If they'd tarried on the way,
No one's told me to this day.
Quickly may a tale be told;
Slowly does a task unfold.
Only this, I know, my friends:
Humpy ran unto those ends
Of the world (for this heard I)
Where the earth meets with the sky,

Where the peasant maid sits high
Spinning flax up in the sky.

Here John bade the earth good-by,
Found himself up in the sky;
Rode along with princely bearing,
Hat atilt to seem more daring.
"This is wonderful! It's great!
Earth's not bad, but at this rate,"
John exclaimed as on they flew
Mid the meadows azure-blue,
"Should the earth with Heaven vie,
It's not fit to line the sky.
After all, what's earth? Look back.
Earth is dirt, and dirt is black.
Here the earth is blue and light,
And extraordinarily bright!
Humpy, look! Look once at least,
Over this way, toward the east,
Where dawn's breaking. Surely this
Is the sky metropolis.
It seems high and grand to me."
John asked Humpy anxiously,

"Lived in that there chamber high
Our Tzar-Princess in the sky?"
Humpy shouted in his flight,
"Here the Sun seeks rest each night.
And the Moon comes here to stay
In the middle of the day."
They approach the gate where grand
Arching crystal pillars stand.
Circling these crystal poles,
Serpents coil in golden scrolls.
On its peak three bright stars glow.
Round the chamber gardens grow
Where on silver branches there,
In their gilded cages, rare
Birds of Paradise day long
Sing for princely ears their song.
Rooms there are the chamber round,
As a Town's girt on the ground.
On its crest a starry cope
Forms the cross of Christian hope.

Humpy galloped in the court.
John dismounted to report

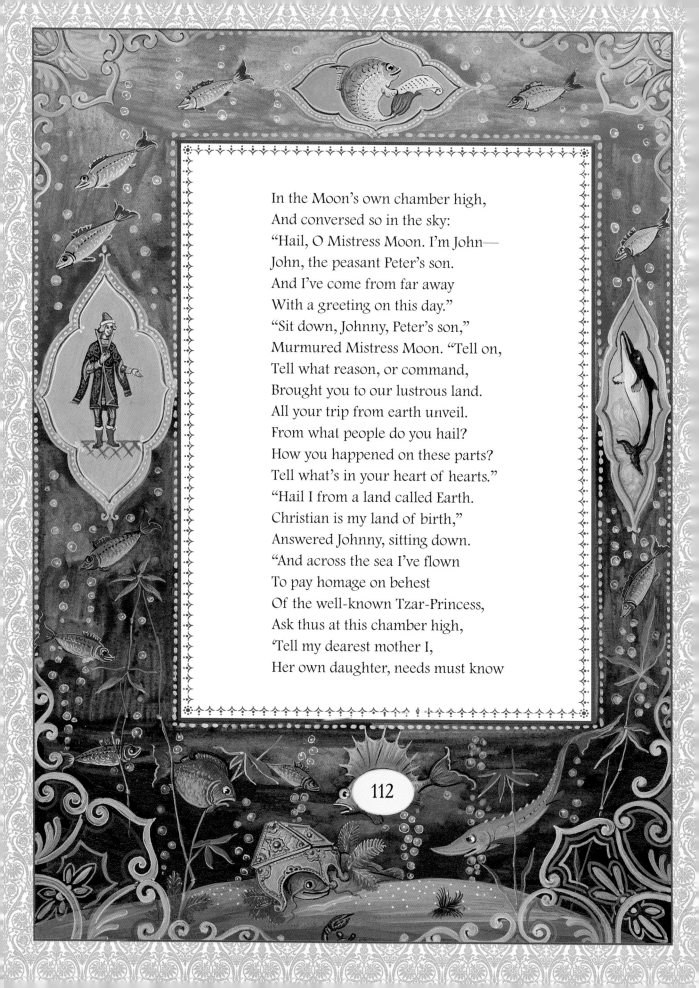

In the Moon's own chamber high,
And conversed so in the sky:
"Hail, O Mistress Moon. I'm John—
John, the peasant Peter's son.
And I've come from far away
With a greeting on this day."
"Sit down, Johnny, Peter's son,"
Murmured Mistress Moon. "Tell on,
Tell what reason, or command,
Brought you to our lustrous land.
All your trip from earth unveil.
From what people do you hail?
How you happened on these parts?
Tell what's in your heart of hearts."
"Hail I from a land called Earth.
Christian is my land of birth,"
Answered Johnny, sitting down.
"And across the sea I've flown
To pay homage on behest
Of the well-known Tzar-Princess,
Ask thus at this chamber high,
'Tell my dearest mother I,
Her own daughter, needs must know

Why she hasn't wished to show
For three days and three long nights
Her loved—was it "face's"—light.
Ask, too, why a Stygian cloud
Does my brother's splendors shroud,
Why through all this gloom he may
Not send me a single ray.'
That was right, I think, for she,
Skillful, spoke her wish to me.
Word for word my sorry head
Can't remember all she said."
"Who's this maid you quote? Confess."
"Why, that maid's the Tzar-Princess."
"Tzar-Princess? Then you are he
Who has taken her from me!"
Mistress Moon cried out, undone.
While our Johnny, Peter's son,
Answered, "Certainly I'm he.
I'm the Tzar's own groom, you see,
And it was the Tzar's command
That I have her there, on hand,
At the palace, in three weeks.
If not, Father Tzar did speak

113

As to how he'd have my head."
Tears of joy the Moon then shed.
Hugged our John, kissed, hugged again,
Called him an endearing name.
"Dearest Johnny, Peter's son,"
Mistress Moon continued on,
"Wondrous news you've brought. I know
Not how best my thanks to show,
For we've sorrowed, grieved, and feared
Since the Princess disappeared.
And that is the reason I,
Mourning in a darkened sky,
Wandered saddened, veiled my light,
Three long days and three long nights.
Three long days I passed unsleeping,
Eating not a crumb, and weeping.
That is why a Stygian cloud
Does my loved son's splendors shroud.
That is why his warming ray
Shone not on the earth by day,
For he missed his sister who
Tzar-Princess is called by you.
Is she well? Oh, tell me, pray!

114

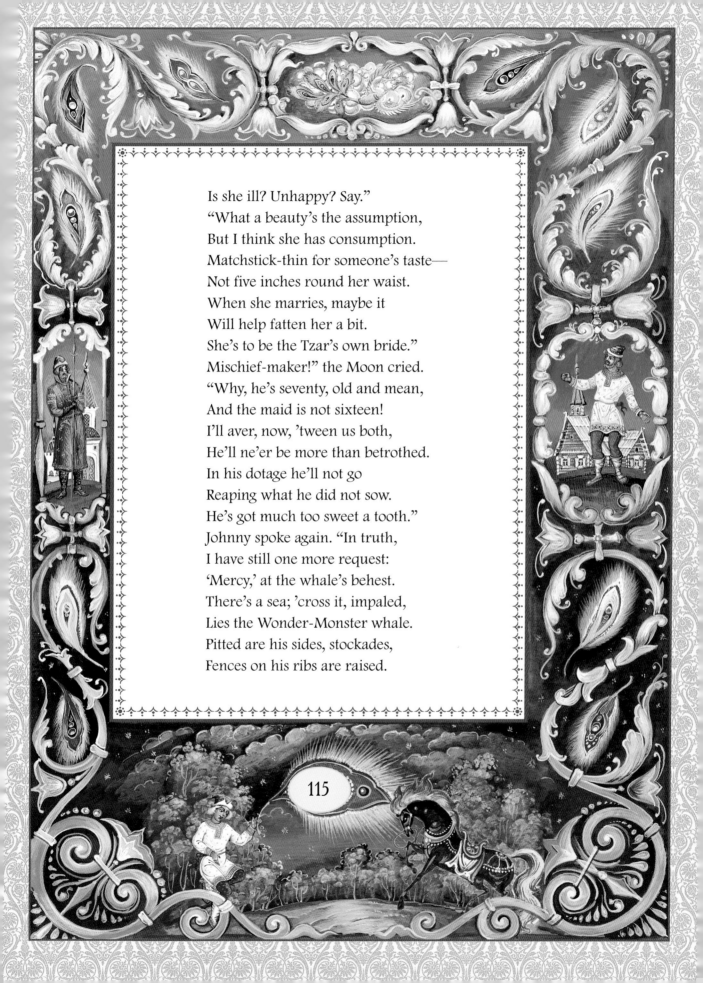

Is she ill? Unhappy? Say."
"What a beauty's the assumption,
But I think she has consumption.
Matchstick-thin for someone's taste—
Not five inches round her waist.
When she marries, maybe it
Will help fatten her a bit.
She's to be the Tzar's own bride."
Mischief-maker!" the Moon cried.
"Why, he's seventy, old and mean,
And the maid is not sixteen!
I'll aver, now, 'tween us both,
He'll ne'er be more than betrothed.
In his dotage he'll not go
Reaping what he did not sow.
He's got much too sweet a tooth."
Johnny spoke again. "In truth,
I have still one more request:
'Mercy,' at the whale's behest.
There's a sea; 'cross it, impaled,
Lies the Wonder-Monster whale.
Pitted are his sides, stockades,
Fences on his ribs are raised.

And the poor thing asked that I
Beg you grant him a reply.
'Soon's his suffering to cease?
How seek pardon and make peace?
Why must he so tortured lie?'"
Ran the lustrous Moon's reply:
"He is punished so because
He ignored the Heavenly laws.
Swallowed he at his own notion
Thirty ships that sailed the ocean.
If he frees them, he will win
Heaven's pardon for his sin.
Heaven will heal his wounds and give
Him innumerable years to live."

Johnny rose and bade good-by
To the bright Moon in the sky,
Hugged her neck, could hardly speak,
Kissed her three times on each cheek.
"Thank you, Johnny, Peter's son,"
Mistress Moon then murmured on,
"From myself and from my son,
For the kindness you have done.

Take my love to the Princess,
So she won't be comfortless.
Tell my loved daughter,
Her own mother, is close by,
Not to grieve, her mourning end,
Soon her miseries will mend.
That no bearded old baboon
But a handsome fine young groom
Will she soon be wedded to.
And good-by. Godspeed to you!"
Johnny bowed his very best,
Mounted Humpy, squared his chest,
Whistled like an errant knight,
Started on his homeward flight.

On the following day he
Once again espied the sea.
Humpy's hoofbeats fall like hail
On the bare bones of the whale.
And again the monster sighs
Pitifully where he lies.
"My request? Tell, friends. Begin.
Will I ever pardon win?"

117

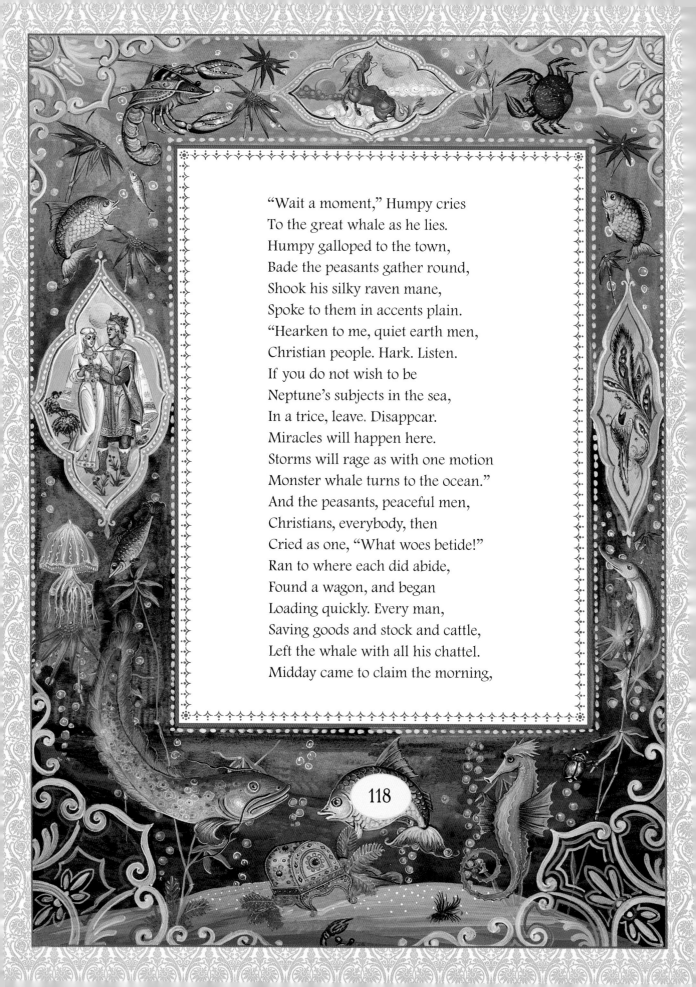

"Wait a moment," Humpy cries
To the great whale as he lies.
Humpy galloped to the town,
Bade the peasants gather round,
Shook his silky raven mane,
Spoke to them in accents plain.
"Hearken to me, quiet earth men,
Christian people. Hark. Listen.
If you do not wish to be
Neptune's subjects in the sea,
In a trice, leave. Disappear.
Miracles will happen here.
Storms will rage as with one motion
Monster whale turns to the ocean."
And the peasants, peaceful men,
Christians, everybody, then
Cried as one, "What woes betide!"
Ran to where each did abide,
Found a wagon, and began
Loading quickly. Every man,
Saving goods and stock and cattle,
Left the whale with all his chattel.
Midday came to claim the morning,

118

And the town at Humpy's warning
Stood bereft of life as though
Conquerors had laid it low!

Humpy gallops on the whale,
Staying near the monster's tail,
Shouting loudly these replies.
"Wonder-Monster whale," he cries,
"You are punished so because
You ignored the Heavenly laws.
For you swallowed at your notion
Thirty ships that sailed the ocean.
If you free them, you will win
Heaven's pardon for your sin.
Heaven will heal your wounds and give
You innumerable years to live."
Having finished speaking, he
Bites his bit to feel more free,
Strains to stretch his jumping reach,
Leaps and lands upon the beach.

And the monster in his groove
Moved like wakening mountains move,

119

Making waves rise in the ocean.
And amidst the sea's commotion
From his jaws the monster whale
Spouted oarsmen, ships, and sail.
Soon such din and clamor broke
That the Ocean Tzar awoke.
Copper cannons boomed loud, long.
Hammered horns blew blasts of song.
Soon alone white sail uncurled;
On the mast a flag unfurled;
And on deck a priest, undone,
Said "Te Deum" and Mass as one.
While a group of oarsmen gay
Sang a sailor's jolly lay;
How upon the deep blue sea,
Wide and comfortable and free,
Ships can sail the cosmic girth,
Even reach the edge of earth.

O'er the waves spread misty light,
And the ships sailed out of sight.
Then the Wonder-Monster whale
Shouted, sounding strong and hale,

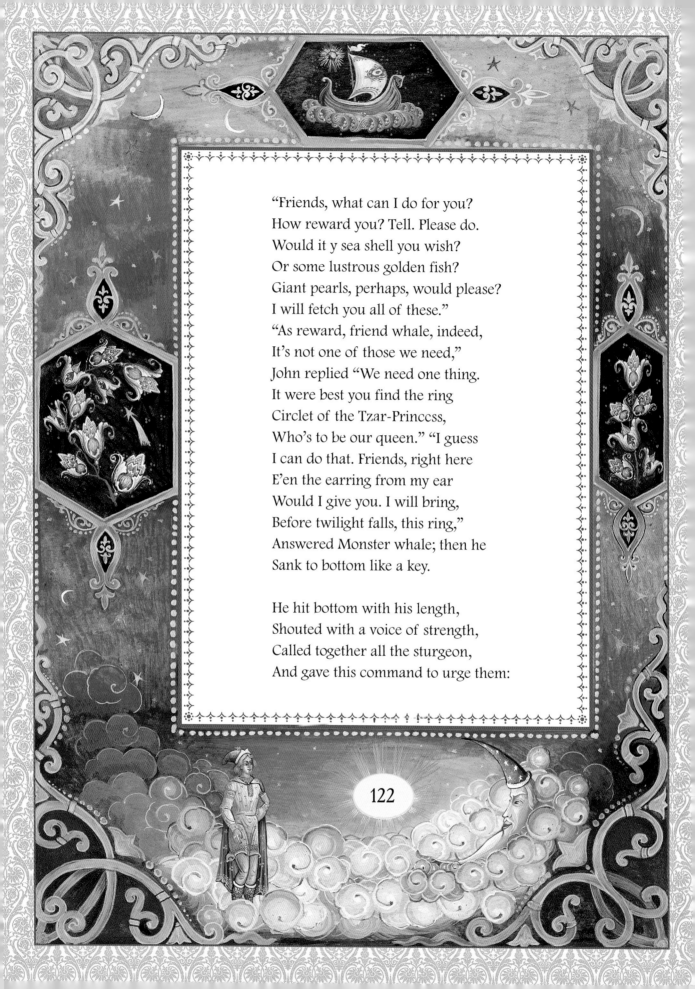

"Friends, what can I do for you?
How reward you? Tell. Please do.
Would it y sea shell you wish?
Or some lustrous golden fish?
Giant pearls, perhaps, would please?
I will fetch you all of these."
"As reward, friend whale, indeed,
It's not one of those we need,"
John replied "We need one thing.
It were best you find the ring
Circlet of the Tzar-Princcss,
Who's to be our queen." "I guess
I can do that. Friends, right here
E'en the earring from my ear
Would I give you. I will bring,
Before twilight falls, this ring,"
Answered Monster whale; then he
Sank to bottom like a key.

He hit bottom with his length,
Shouted with a voice of strength,
Called together all the sturgeon,
And gave this command to urge them:

"Find ere twilight falls and bring
Me the Tzar-Princess' ring,
In a chest on bottom hidden.
He who does as he is bidden
Will receive the honored rank
Of knight-councilor in thanks.
Understand? Bestir yourselves!
Fill my stern command, or else—"
And each sturgeon bowed his head
Calmly on his mission sped.

In an hour, or two or three,
Two white sturgeon quietly
Swam up to the Monster whale
To report in fine detail.
"Don't be angry, mighty tzar,
The whole ocean near and far
Have we searched and swum for naught,
Found no sign of what we sought.
And to carry out your task,
It's the burfish you must ask.
For he roams in every sea,
Knows the ring most certainly;

123

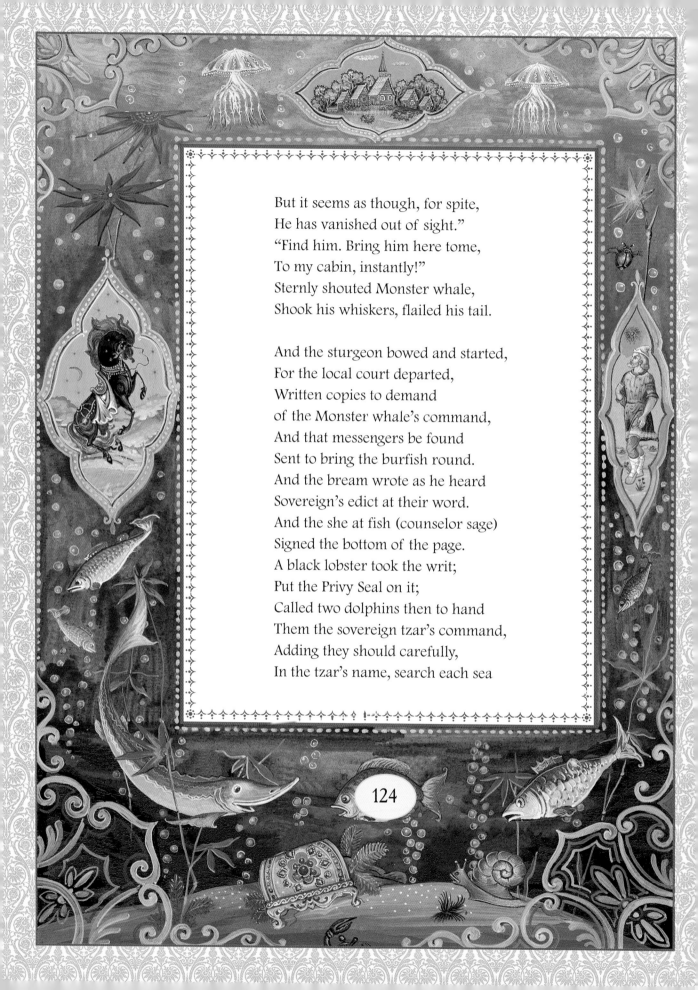

But it seems as though, for spite,
He has vanished out of sight."
"Find him. Bring him here tome,
To my cabin, instantly!"
Sternly shouted Monster whale,
Shook his whiskers, flailed his tail.

And the sturgeon bowed and started,
For the local court departed,
Written copies to demand
of the Monster whale's command,
And that messengers be found
Sent to bring the burfish round.
And the bream wrote as he heard
Sovereign's edict at their word.
And the she at fish (counselor sage)
Signed the bottom of the page.
A black lobster took the writ;
Put the Privy Seal on it;
Called two dolphins then to hand
Them the sovereign tzar's command,
Adding they should carefully,
In the tzar's name, search each sea

Till they find the shiftless scold,
Stray burfish, swashbuckler bold,
Bring him back from where he be
To the sovereign instantly.
And the dolphins bowed and started,
On their search straightway departed.

For an hour they search the sea,
Then the rivers flowing free;
Swim each lake and every pond;
Hunt in every strait and sound;
Seek the burfish everywhere
And return home in despair,
Feeling tearful from chagrin!
When they chance to hear a din,
Shouting, argument, rebuttal,
Emanating from a puddle.
Toward the pool the dolphins start;
To the bottom straightway dart,
Where behind some reeds in battle
Crucian carp and burfish prattle.
"Hush the noise! A plague on you!
Why, the row you've raised would do

125

Justice to two mighty warriors,"
To them shout the dolphin couriers.
"Why butt in?" the burfish cries,
To the dolphins so replies.
"Trifling's not my way. One blow
And I'll lay the whole lot low!"
"Why, you shiftless stray, you scold,
Bully and swashbuckler bold,
Worthless tramp, whose only joys
Are to drift, to fight, make noise.
Home? Not home is your life spent,
We'vc no time for argument.
Here we have our tzar's command.
'Swim to him,' is his demand."

So they take the mischief-maker
By his bristles. With the faker
Home the dolphins swim, The stray
Scolds and fights to get away.
"Clement brothers, please permit,
Let me stay and fight a bit.
Why, that crucian—cursed be he—
Yesterday insulted me,

Blackened me with slanders loud
Here before a goodly crowd."
Long the struggling burfish riots
But at last calms down and quiets.
Still they drag him, mischief-maker,
By his bristles, pull the faker.
All in silence journey home
Till before the Tzar they come.

"You've been long in coming. Pray,
Hostile son, where did you stray?"
Shouted Monster whale, displeased.
Feel the burfish on his knees,
Straightway did his sin confess,
Humbly begged forgiveness.
"Heaven grant you be reprieved!"
Said the mighty whale, relieved.
"But, for mercy, I demand
That you first fill my command."
"Glad to help you! Glad to please!"
Squeaked the burfish on his knees.
"You who range in every sea,
You must know the ring that we

Seek, the Tzar-Princess' ring."
"Yes, and I can find the thing!"
"If that's so, then on your way,
Fetch it here without delay!"

Bowing meekly, set for trouble,
Exits burfish, still bent double;
Fights the servants going out:
Trails a flirting dace about;
Meets six sprats and forthwith goes,
Punches all six in the nose.
On accomplishing these deeds,
Swiftly to a pool he speeds
In its sandy depths to quest;
Digs around and finds a chest
Weighing 'most four thousand pounds.
"This will be a job!" he frowns.
And the burfish shouts a plea,
Cans the shad from every sea.
And the shad take heart, feel strong,
Try to pull the chest along.
Only grunts and sighs are heard:

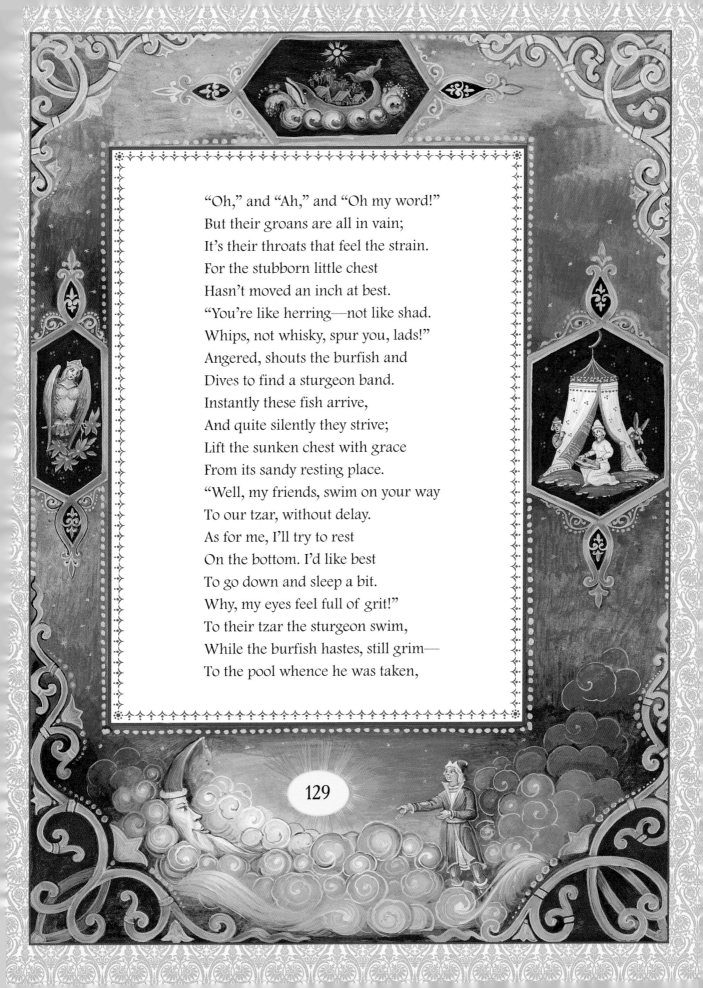

"Oh," and "Ah," and "Oh my word!"
But their groans are all in vain;
It's their throats that feel the strain.
For the stubborn little chest
Hasn't moved an inch at best.
"You're like herring—not like shad.
Whips, not whisky, spur you, lads!"
Angered, shouts the burfish and
Dives to find a sturgeon band.
Instantly these fish arrive,
And quite silently they strive;
Lift the sunken chest with grace
From its sandy resting place.
"Well, my friends, swim on your way
To our tzar, without delay.
As for me, I'll try to rest
On the bottom. I'd like best
To go down and sleep a bit.
Why, my eyes feel full of grit!"
To their tzar the sturgeon swim,
While the burfish hastes, still grim—
To the pool whence he was taken,

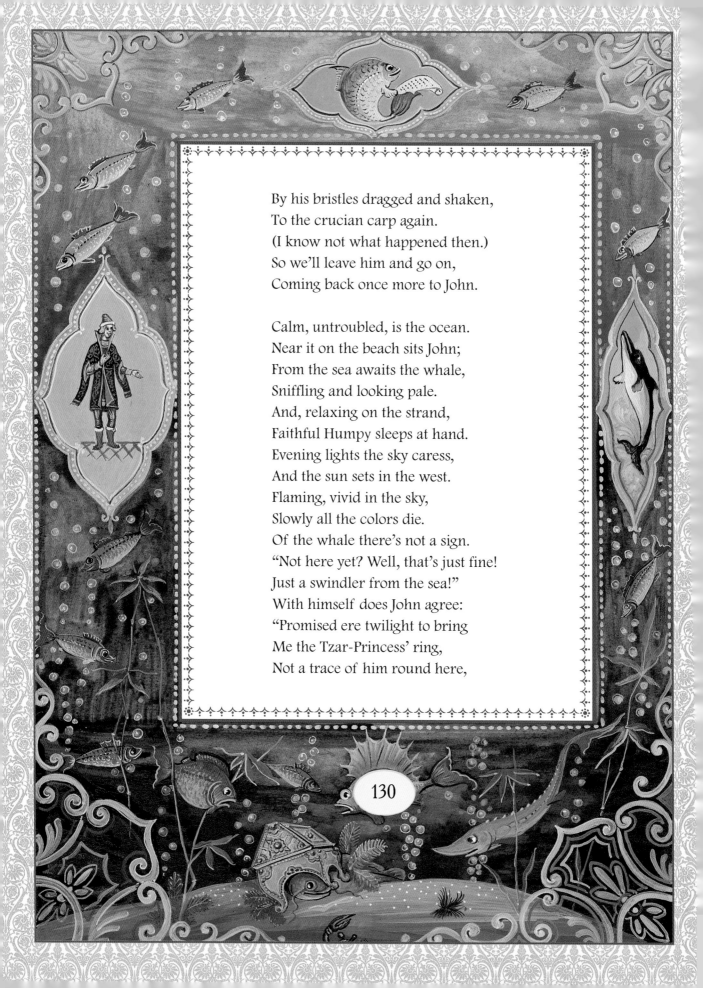

By his bristles dragged and shaken,
To the crucian carp again.
(I know not what happened then.)
So we'll leave him and go on,
Coming back once more to John.

Calm, untroubled, is the ocean.
Near it on the beach sits John;
From the sea awaits the whale,
Sniffling and looking pale.
And, relaxing on the strand,
Faithful Humpy sleeps at hand.
Evening lights the sky caress,
And the sun sets in the west.
Flaming, vivid in the sky,
Slowly all the colors die.
Of the whale there's not a sign.
"Not here yet? Well, that's just fine!
Just a swindler from the sea!"
With himself does John agree:
"Promised ere twilight to bring
Me the Tzar-Princess' ring,
Not a trace of him round here,

Or his wretched tooth-filled leer.
And the sun has set. Who knows—"
Suddenly a sea storm blows,
And the Monster whale appears,
Speaks, and banishes John's fears.
"For the kindness shown tome
I have kept my word, you see."
And with this the red chest lands,
Dully clanking on the sands,
And the shore shakes from its weight.
"Now we're quits, but may I state:
If you should have need of me
Call, and I will helpful be.
For your kindness, grateful I
Will remain. And so good-by."
And the monster spoke no more,
Splashed, sank to the ocean floor.

All alert, the pony wakes;
Gets upon his feet and shakes;
Looks at Johnny's sunny smile;
Leaps four times in fancy style.
"He's a wonder-whale to pay,

Promptly meet his debt this way!
Thank you, Wonder-Monster fish!"
Humpy shouts that parting wish.
"Well, my master, time to dress,
Homeward to our efforts press.
Three days passed. The deadline's near.
It's tomorrow we appear.
Why, the old man must be dying!"
Johnny answers, "No denying.
I can't lift this, to my sorrow.
It's some strength I'd have to borrow.
Though it's small, the chest's compact;
Or perhaps that old whale stacked
In a hundred fiends. I'm stuck,
Though three times I've tried. What luck!
It's too heavy to be stirred!"
Humpy answers not a word,
Prods the chest; his small hoof lifts it,
Like a pebble deftly shifts it
To his neck with easy grace.
"Climb, up, Johnny! Take your place!
With the morrow reckonings come,
And we're far away from home."

On the fourth day with the dawn
In the city rode our John.
Ran the Tzar to haste the meeting.
"Where's my ring?" his feverish greeting.
John got off the little horse
Proud to answer, thus discourse.
"I have brought the little chest.
It looks small, but should it fall,
It could crush Old Nick. That's all."
The Tzar called an archer band,
Gave a quick, precise command
As to where the chest be brought
Then himself the Princess sought.

"They have found your ring, my heart,"
Honeyed, did the Tzar's words start.
"Now," he said, "I'll name the day;
Nothing more stands in our way.
On the morrow, little dove,
You and I will wed, my love.
Would it please you, for it ought,
See your ring that has been brought?
It lies in my palace now!"

134

Then the Princess did avow,
"Yes, I know. But you must see
That this marriage still can't be!"
"And why not, my little dove,
For my heart is filled with love?
Pray don't think me bold," he pled.
"I can scarce wait to be wed.
Should you spurn me—grieving, I
By tomorrow morn would die!
Sweet maid, be not merciless!"
Thus replied the Tzar-Princess,
"Look, O Tzar—you're old; you're gray.
I am but sixteen. How, pray,
Can we marry? Near and far
Laughingstock of every tzar
Will we be. Each tzar will sneer,
'Grandpa robbed the crib, we hear!'"
And the angered Tzar cried out,
"Let them laugh, just once—you'll see
They'll ne'er get away from me!
I'll enslave their empires, trace
And destroy each sovereign's race!"
"Even if they'd not laugh, we

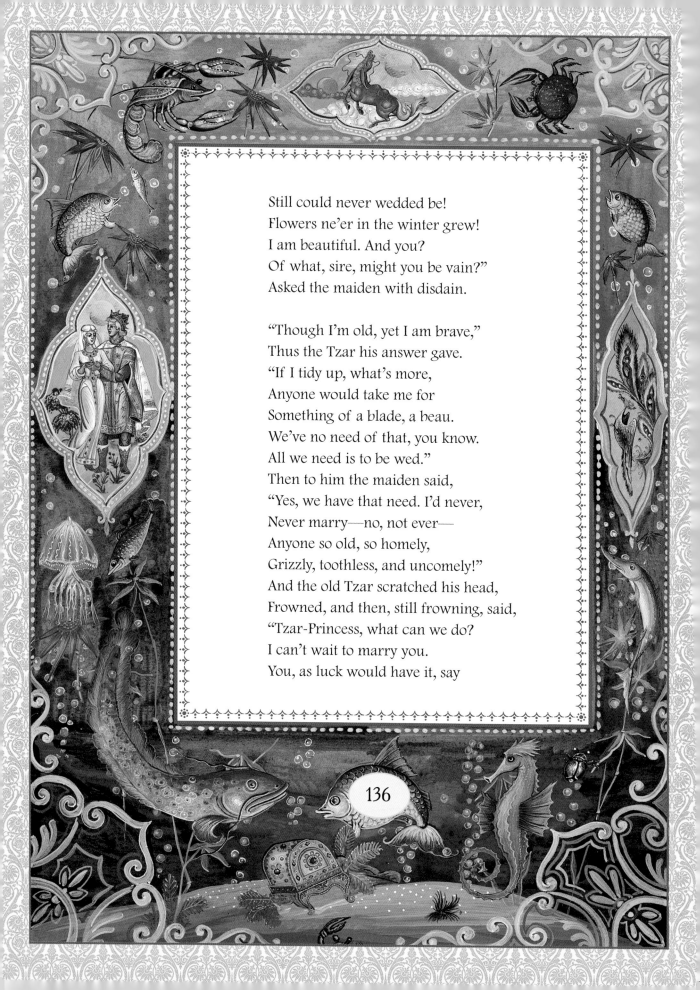

Still could never wedded be!
Flowers ne'er in the winter grew!
I am beautiful. And you?
Of what, sire, might you be vain?"
Asked the maiden with disdain.

"Though I'm old, yet I am brave,"
Thus the Tzar his answer gave.
"If I tidy up, what's more,
Anyone would take me for
Something of a blade, a beau.
We've no need of that, you know.
All we need is to be wed."
Then to him the maiden said,
"Yes, we have that need. I'd never,
Never marry—no, not ever—
Anyone so old, so homely,
Grizzly, toothless, and uncomely!"
And the old Tzar scratched his head,
Frowned, and then, still frowning, said,
"Tzar-Princess, what can we do?
I can't wait to marry you.
You, as luck would have it, say

136

'I won't wed,' and cause delay."
"I'll not wed an old man," then
Did the maid begin again.
"If you'll change into a beau
Off to church I'll gladly go!"
"Keep in mind, fair maid, pray do,
I can't be reborn tor you.
Wonder-work's on Heaven's plane."
Said the Princess, "I'll explain.
Spare yourself not; hear this truth,
And recapture your lost youth.
At tomorrow's dawn command
That they fetch three caldrons and
Set those caldrons up outside
In that open courtyard wide.
Build a fire beneath each one.
Then, brimful, when that is done,
Pour iced water in one pot,
Make the second scalding-hot,
And with sweet milk fill the last.
Keep the sweet milk boiling fast.
Then, if you still wish to marry
And regain your youth, don't tarry;

But, unclothed, quite nude and brave,
Plunge into the milk and bathe.
Then leap in the scalding-hot.
Last try the iced-water pot.
Sire, you'll be, believe me, then
Much the handsomest of men!"

Silence reigned within that room.
The Tzar only called his groom.
"Will it be the sea? How far?"
Asked our Johnny of the Tzar.
"No, Your Highness, you're refused.
From that last trip I'm confused.
Nothing'll ever make me go!"
"Johnny, that's not it! Oh, no!
On the morrow I'll command
That they set three pots out, and
Build a fire beneath each one.
Then, brimful, when that is done,
Pour iced water in one pot,
Make the second scalding-hot,
And with sweet milk fill the last.
Keep the sweet milk boiling fast.

You will bathe, at my request,
As a kind of simple test,
In each giant metal pot.
Milk, two waters, that's the lot."
"Ask a service, in this guise,"
John began to sermonize.
"Why, it's pigs one scalds, and chickens,
Turkeys, other fowl. The dickens!
Look at me! I'm not a chick,
Turkey, or a pig! Look quick!
In the water that's ice-cold
I could bathe, of course. But hold!
When you scald, then rest assured
There's no way I can be lured.
With all wiles, O Tzar, have done;
Stop imposing on me, John."
And the Tzar's beard shook in ire.
"Wrangling's not what I desire!"
And he shouted in his wake,
"Mind, at dawn, you'll undertake
To fulfill this, my command,
Or be tortured. Understand?
First I'll have you racked, then cease,

Tear you slowly piece from piece!
Plague that is of evil bred,
Filth, begone!" Tears Johnny shed;
Trailed up to the loft of hay,
Where his humpback pony lay.

"Why is Johnny sad?" he pled.
"Why hangs low his bonnie head?"
Gently asked the little horse.
"It's the Tzar again, of course.
Has our groom some new plan? Tell!"
Round the pony's neck John fell,
Kissed him, hugged him with full force.
"Woe is me, my little horse!
The Tzar rids himself of me
Think you, by his own decree!
Orders me to bathe undressed
In huge caldrons for some test.
There's iced water in one pot,
While the second's scalding-hot.
In the third, milk boils. What now?"
Then the pony did avow,
"Here's a chore that is a chore,

140

Needing all my help and more!
I can't help but say 'twere better
That we'd left the Firebird's feather.
It's the cause, the evil source,
Of your troubles and remorse.
Hush. Don't cry. With Heaven's aid
All your woes will be allayed.
I, myself, would rather perish
Than desert you, whom I cherish.
When the morn breaks in the skies
In the courtyard, at sunrise,
First undress, just as you should.
Ask the Tzar, 'Your Highness, would
You give orders, Majesty,
Have my Humpy brought to me?
One last parting! One good-by!'
And the old Tzar must comply.
First I'll switch my tail, then race,
In each caldron dip my face,
Sprinkle on you twice, and give
One sharp whistle. Look alive!
Watch each move. Plunge, at the last,
In the milk that's boiling fast,

Then leap in the scalding-hot,
Last try the iced-water pot.
Now, when all your prayers are said,
Go off peacefully to bed."

Bright and early in the morning
Humpy woke John with the warning,
"Wake up, master. Cease your dreaming.
Time to start your woes redeeming."
Johnny woke and scratched his head;
Stretched himself; got out of bed,
By the Holy Church to pray;
To the courtyard made his way.

There the pots were being heated.
Near them, in a row, were seated
Coachmen, lackeys, cooks—in short,
All the servants of the court.
Zealously they added wood;
Talked of Johnny when they could;
Slyly letting fall a smile,
Softly laughed once in a while.

Soon the palace doors swing wide
For the Tzar and his fair bride,
On the steps they start preparing
To observe the hero's daring.
"Johnny boy, undress. Prepare.
Take a bath in those pots there!"
Is the Tzar's command to John.
John takes off what he has on,
Saying nothing in reply.
While the Princess drops her eye
And, unmindful, young, and proud,
Veils her beauty in a shroud.

To the caldrons John does climb,
Looks in, scratches, bides his time.
"Johnny—leap. Don't stand about!"
Restlessly the Tzar does shout
"Go ahead—do as you should!"
Johnny asks," Your Highness, would
You give orders, Majesty,
Have my Humpy brought to me?
One last parting! One good-by!"
And the old Tzar must comply,

Gives command that Humpy be
Brought to him immediately.
For the horse a servant hied,
Led him in, and stepped aside.

Humpy switched his tail, did race,
In each caldron dipped his face,
Sprinkled on John twice, and blew
One sharp whistle. Johnny threw
Humpy a quick look and lunged,
In the first pot promptly plunged,
Tried the second, third, and so
Very handsome did he grow
That a mere tale cannot tell
Nor a pen describe it well.
Having finished, donned his dress,
Made a bow to the Princess.
Glanced around. Felt heartened. Took
On a proud, patrician look.

"Wonderful!" arose the cry.
"No one's heard, not you, not I,
That one could so handsome be."

They disrobed the Tzar. Then he
Crossed himself, and drew a breath—
Leaped right in, and boiled to death!

Then the Princess took a stand,
Signaled "Silence" with her hand,
Raised her veil, spoke standing there
To the servants to declare:
"'Long life' was the Tzar's decree.
I, I would your sovereign be.
Does that please you? Answer now.
If that please you, then avow
Him who is my groom-to-be
Sovereign Tzar, this day with me."
Done, the Princess turned about;
Hushed, and pointed Johnny out.
And the people cried, "We do!
Why, we'd go through fire for you!
Your success is the condition
That affords John recognition."

Tzar and bride the verdict heed,
To the Holy Church proceed,

And together, hand in hand,
At the bridal altar stand.

Cannons from the fort boom strong.
Hammered horns blow blasts of song.
All the cellars open wide;
Liquor kegs are rolled outside.
And a deafening roar rings out
As the tippling people shout,
"Health, O Tzar! Health to the bride!
Sovereign Beauty at his side.

Seated, feasting, row on row,
Where the wines in rivers flow,
At the oaken palace boards
Are the noblemen and lords.
And my heart was glad. Indeed,
I was there. Drank beer, wine, mead,
Most of which, 'tis sad to note,
Trickled down my beard, not throat.

Contents

On the Author

Pyotr Pavlovich Yershov was born on February 22 (March 6, New Style), 1815, in the village of Bezrukovo, Ishimsky District, Tobolsk Province. When he was ten years old, his father, a police officer, was transferred to serve in Tobolsk.

In 1830 Pyotr Yershov graduated with honors from the gymnasium and enrolled at the Faculty of Philosophy and Law in St. Petersburg University. But he was not a very diligent student and graduated from the university only because of good fortune: he prepared to answer only one question card at his examinations, and it was precisely this card that Yershov was lucky to pick up. He lamented his own laziness and regretted about being insufficiently well educated. "Here I am," he would say, "a University graduate, who has no command of any foreign language."

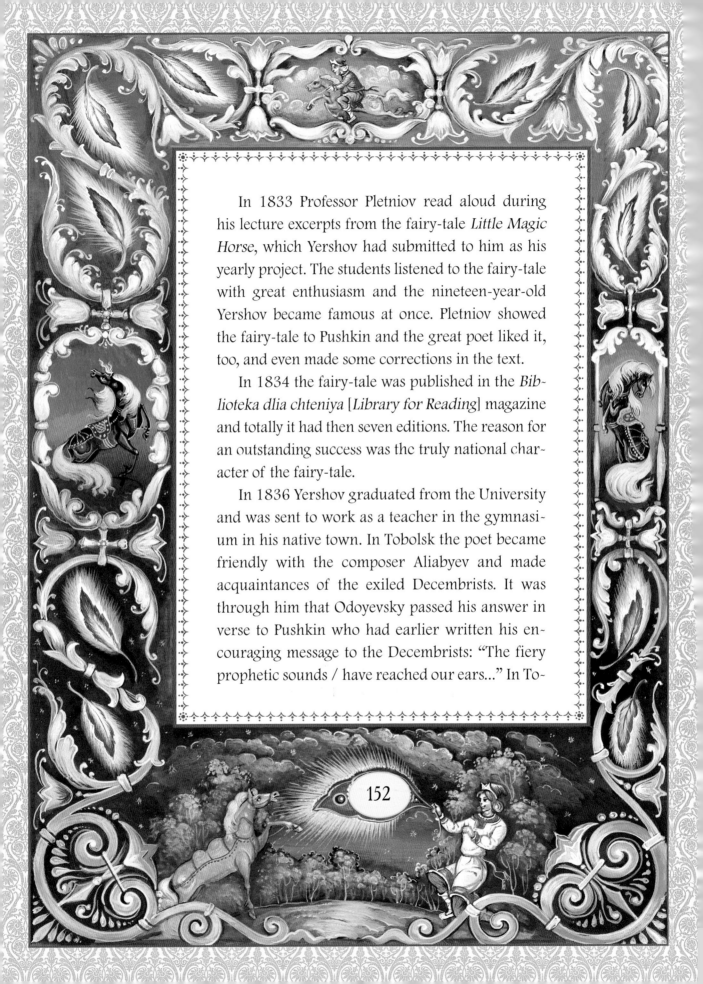

In 1833 Professor Pletniov read aloud during his lecture excerpts from the fairy-tale *Little Magic Horse*, which Yershov had submitted to him as his yearly project. The students listened to the fairy-tale with great enthusiasm and the nineteen-year-old Yershov became famous at once. Pletniov showed the fairy-tale to Pushkin and the great poet liked it, too, and even made some corrections in the text.

In 1834 the fairy-tale was published in the *Biblioteka dlia chteniya* [*Library for Reading*] magazine and totally it had then seven editions. The reason for an outstanding success was the truly national character of the fairy-tale.

In 1836 Yershov graduated from the University and was sent to work as a teacher in the gymnasium in his native town. In Tobolsk the poet became friendly with the composer Aliabyev and made acquaintances of the exiled Decembrists. It was through him that Odoyevsky passed his answer in verse to Pushkin who had earlier written his encouraging message to the Decembrists: "The fiery prophetic sounds / have reached our ears..." In To-

152

bolsk Yershov continued to create poetry, wrote an essay about a Siberian Cossack, the poem *Suzge*, the story *Merchant Bazim*, but these works proved to be just ordinary creations. Yershov failed to repeat the success of his inspired fairy-tale created during his student years. Being a creative person, he had many good ideas, but they were not realized. According to his son, Yershov left an archive of seven carefully bound volumes, but they have not yet been found.

Perhaps the writer would be able to become famous, but his fate was decided in a different way. Yershov fell in love with the daughter of the former headmaster of the gymnasium, a widow with several children. Initially Serafima Leshova refused to marry the young teacher, but in 1839 their wedding took place and a completely different life began. He had to earn a living for his family every day, and this concern for well-being was not favorable for the development of his literary talent and inspiration. The earlier dreams of ethnographic research also vanished. Moreover, the poet had serious problems

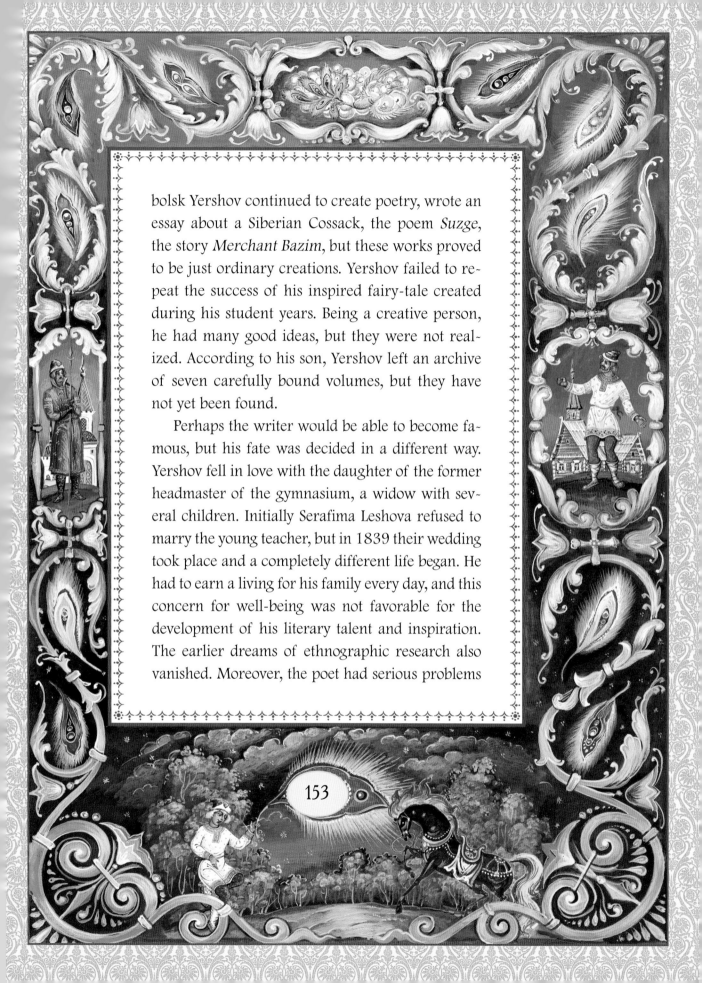

153

with his service owing to an unfriendly attitude of the gymnasium director E. M. Kachurin.

As a teacher Yershov tried to create a new schooling course, and wanted to introduce some changes in Russian literature. But since he has never published his projects, only vague memories about them have reached us.

In 1844 Yershov was appointed a school inspector, but he dreamed of becoming the gymnasium head. When the Director Kachurin took a three-month leave of absence and went to St. Petersburg, rumors spread that he was not going to come back either to Tobolsk or to the school. Yershov then wrote to Professor Pletniov, with whom he maintained friendly relations since the university studies, about his desire to occupy the position of the gymnasium head and asked the professor for his help. It is not known whether it was thanks to Pletniov's recommendation or just a natural course of events, but after thirteen years of work in the gymnasium Yershov was put at its head.

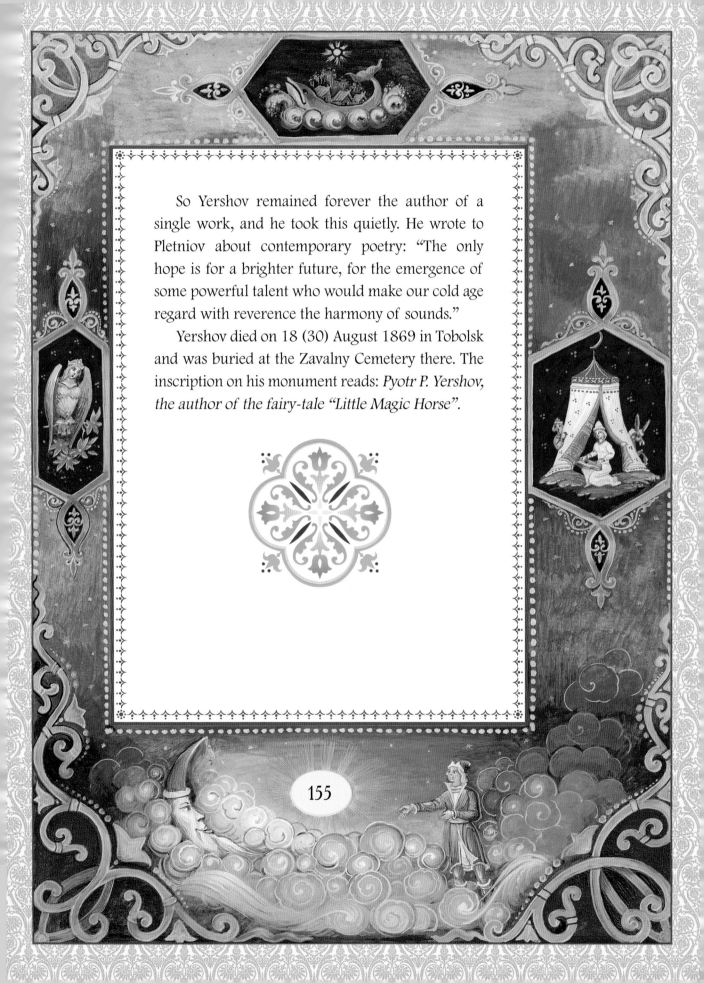

So Yershov remained forever the author of a single work, and he took this quietly. He wrote to Pletniov about contemporary poetry: "The only hope is for a brighter future, for the emergence of some powerful talent who would make our cold age regard with reverence the harmony of sounds."

Yershov died on 18 (30) August 1869 in Tobolsk and was buried at the Zavalny Cemetery there. The inscription on his monument reads: *Pyotr P. Yershov, the author of the fairy-tale "Little Magic Horse".*

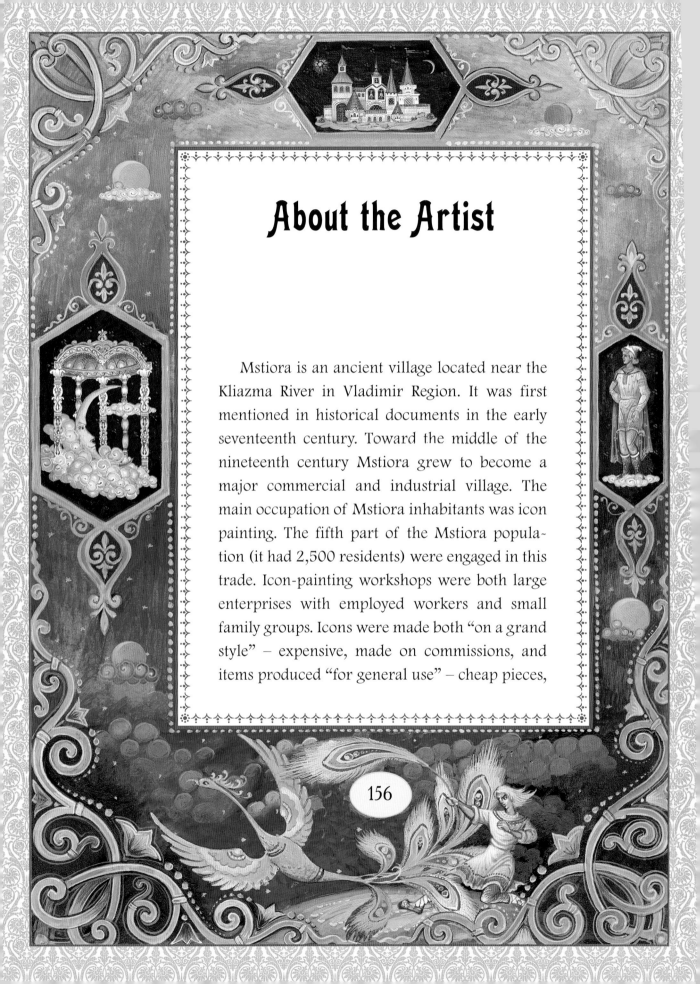

About the Artist

Mstiora is an ancient village located near the Kliazma River in Vladimir Region. It was first mentioned in historical documents in the early seventeenth century. Toward the middle of the nineteenth century Mstiora grew to become a major commercial and industrial village. The main occupation of Mstiora inhabitants was icon painting. The fifth part of the Mstiora population (it had 2,500 residents) were engaged in this trade. Icon-painting workshops were both large enterprises with employed workers and small family groups. Icons were made both "on a grand style" – expensive, made on commissions, and items produced "for general use" – cheap pieces,

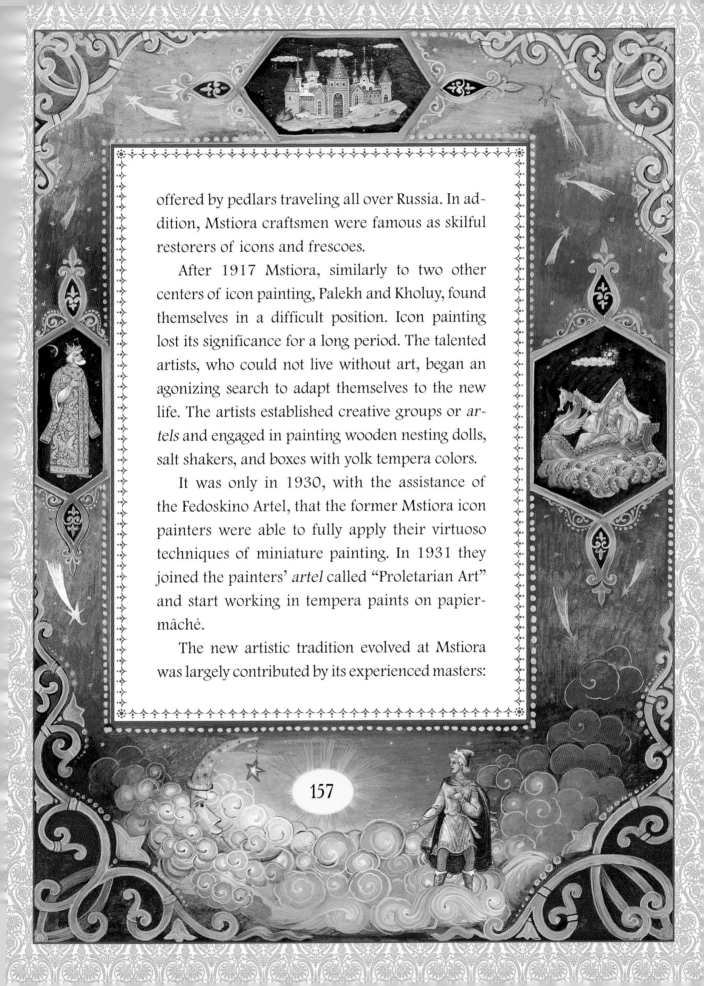

offered by pedlars traveling all over Russia. In addition, Mstiora craftsmen were famous as skilful restorers of icons and frescoes.

After 1917 Mstiora, similarly to two other centers of icon painting, Palekh and Kholuy, found themselves in a difficult position. Icon painting lost its significance for a long period. The talented artists, who could not live without art, began an agonizing search to adapt themselves to the new life. The artists established creative groups or *artels* and engaged in painting wooden nesting dolls, salt shakers, and boxes with yolk tempera colors.

It was only in 1930, with the assistance of the Fedoskino Artel, that the former Mstiora icon painters were able to fully apply their virtuoso techniques of miniature painting. In 1931 they joined the painters' *artel* called "Proletarian Art" and start working in tempera paints on papier-mâché.

The new artistic tradition evolved at Mstiora was largely contributed by its experienced masters:

157

N.P. Fangs, A.I. Briagin, A.F. Kotiagin, A.A. Serebrianikov, E.V. Yurin, A.M. Merkuryev, and V.I. Sovin. All of them had a good training in icon painting and a fine command of the technique based on traditional methods of icon painting.

Mstiora lacquer miniatures, created by the former painters, are remarkable for their exquisite design and a wealth and harmony of color schemes. It is no accident that Mstiora artistic products received awards at international exhibitions in Paris, London, and Brussels.

The recent art of miniature painting at Mstiora has also been rich in talented artists. One of them is Vladimir Nemov, a graduate of the Madorov Art College at Mstiora (1975). His manner of painting is elaborate and varied. He is able to attain an amazing wealth of colors combined with gentle tonal transitions.

In addition to traditional Mstiora lacquer wares, the artist Nemov illustrates books revealing his extraordinary imagination. Among the